A SUPERVISOR'S GUIDE TO (SAFETY) LEADERSHIP

PREVENTING INJURY IN THE WORKPLACE

A SUPERVISOR'S GUIDE TO (SAFETY) LEADERSHIP

JUDY AGNEW, Ph.D

Performance Management Publications (PMP)

PMP

Performance Management Publications (PMP)
3344 Peachtree Road NE, Suite 1050
Atlanta, GA 30326
678.904.6140

ISBN-10: 0-937100-27-7
ISBN-13: 978-0-937-100-27-1

Printed in the United States of America by ViaTech Publishing Solutions

2 3 4 5 6 7

Lisa Smith, Art Director (cover and text design)
Gail Snyder, Editor

PMP is a division of Aubrey Daniels International, Inc.

PMP books are available at special discounts for bulk purchases by corporations, institutions, and other organizations. For more information, please call 678.904.6140.

DEDICATION

This book is dedicated to Aubrey Daniels.

*If I have seen further,
it is by standing on the shoulders of giants.*[1]

[1.] Isaac Newton, 1676

WHAT PEOPLE ARE SAYING ABOUT

A SUPERVISOR'S GUIDE TO (SAFETY) LEADERSHIP

The truth is that most frontline supervisors are managing people in ways that limit the results they get. This book helps unlock the mystery around creating a great safety culture and enables frontline supervisors to see their role in it. "A Supervisor's Guide to (Safety) Leadership" helps them see that the magic is in taking care of their people and shows them how they can do that.

—**Gary Catapano, Senior Vice President of Safety**
First Student, Inc.

Simple and yet so powerful, Agnew provides a combination of practical tips and tools from a supervisor's perspective that demystifies the approach to achieving sustainable safety improvement.

—**Maria Krysa, Director, Olin Responsible Care & Quality**
Olin Corporation

Frontline supervisors are the linchpins of safety...and this book is the keystone, the linchpin, for safety leadership success. This gets to the most critical step of a successful safety process— enlightening and teaching how to engage the workforce. To pull it all together, "A Supervisor's Guide to (Safety) Leadership" is THE formula. A must-read!

—**David F. Julian, Vice President Safety and Environmental (Retired) Norfolk Southern Corporation**

If only I had this book 30 years ago as a frontline production supervisor—I now see how my unintentional use of negative reinforcement stifled the discretionary effort of my people. This book is not only applicable to a frontline supervisor but to all layers of management in an organization. Understanding the power of positive reinforcement as it relates to the behaviors of those we work with can yield a more productive and safe work environment for all. The easy part of this process is reading the material. The challenge is being diligent in using these tools and techniques. But in doing so, you will be surprised by how much more effective you become.

—**J.W. (Jim) Latham III, Director of Positively CONSOL CONSOL Energy**

Dr. Judy Agnew's latest book, "A Supervisor's Guide to (Safety) Leadership," provides practical guidance for how front-line supervisors can positively impact safety. This book appeals to safety leaders at all levels, but the focus on tools for men and women leading from the ground gets right at the heart of how to make a big difference. While leadership top down is always critical, frontline supervisors need practical tools to help them achieve safety excellence and build a safety culture that leads to sustainable results—while at the same time managing produc- tion and quality demands. Dr. Agnew's book lays out clear and sensible, easy to follow, bite-sized steps that all supervisors can take to make a positive impact on the health and safety of the people who work for them.

—**Karin Stamy, System Director Safety Norfolk Southern Corporation**

ACKNOWLEDGMENTS

It never seems right to have just one author on a book like this. While I typed out the words, the content came from my experiences and interactions with many people over many years. All of my extraordinary colleagues at Aubrey Daniels International (ADI) helped either directly or indirectly with this book. In particular I want to thank Tom Spencer who has supported me in all I have done and makes everything he edits better. Cloyd Hyten, Bart Sevin, and Dave Uhl provided feedback that improved the book and have shaped my thinking and consulting work in positive ways. Julie Terling helped keep the content real and readable. Laura Lee Glass fixed my grammatical gaffs and inconsistencies. Lisa Smith made the book look beautiful. I am also indebted to all of the clients I have had the privilege to work with over the years. I learned from all of you.

Finally, I want to thank my family for their love and support. My mom Joyce, my brother Blaine, and my sister Claire always cheer me on. My father Hinds, I think, would be proud. My wonderful husband Bruce encourages me and picks up the slack when my work takes me away. And my amazing children, Matthew and Kianna—watching them become thoughtful, intelligent, kind, funny, and loving people has been the greatest joy in my life.

TABLE OF CONTENTS

CHAPTER 1

INTRODUCTION: A NOTE TO FRONTLINE SUPERVISORS

"There are risks and costs to action. But they are far less than the long-range risks of comfortable inaction."
—John F. Kennedy

Why Should You Read This Book?

The short answer is because lives depend on your safety leadership.

The long answer has to do with your critical role in this complex thing called *safety*. A safe workplace takes a coordinated effort on the part of all employees. Senior leaders establish safety-oriented vision and values; middle managers put into effect safety management systems, procedures, and accountability; and front-line employees complete the work as safely as possible. Frontline supervisors have perhaps the most crucial role—they are the *linchpins* of safety.

Frontline supervisors are the linchpins of safety.

Wikipedia defines the word *linchpin* as "something (or someone) that holds the various elements of a complicated structure together." Frontline supervision is where safety comes together, where the vision and values are executed, where procedures are complied with, where decisions are implemented, and where safety can be seen. It is the moment-by-moment decisions and actions of the frontline supervisor that ensure the safety of frontline performers.

Linchpins have to be strong. There are pressures from every direction: your boss, your peers, and your direct reports. There are pressures around all of the key performance indicators: production, quality, customer service, employee satisfaction, and of course, safety. The list of responsibilities is long and frontline supervisors are pushed and pulled every day. It is easy to get distracted by seemingly competing priorities. But here's the bottom line—lives are in your hands. Your team depends on you to help them stay alive and unharmed. Nothing in your job is more important than preventing injury in the workplace.

Reading this book won't magically transform you into the perfect frontline supervisor. It will, however, give you practical tools to improve your safety management and safety leadership. While the tools are based on the science of behavior, the scientific discussion is kept to a minimum. The most essential information from the science is listed at the end of

Good safety leadership is good people leadership.

this chapter. If you want to learn more about the science, recommended readings are provided. This book is organized around nine essential safety leadership practices. It's possible you have mastered some of these already or maybe you need to work on all nine. Mastering these leadership practices will lead to improvements in safety. But the practices apply beyond safety. It turns out that good *safety* leadership is really good *people* leadership.

One final note—reading won't improve your leadership skills so be prepared to try what you read. Each chapter ends with a short section called "Start Today" which, as the title suggests, gives you a few specific things you can start working on immediately. Try some or all of them, assess how they work, refine, customize, and repeat. Figure out ways to make these tips work for you so they become part of your every day. ***Start today.***

Essential information for safety leadership from the science of behavior follows:

1. The ABC Model (Antecedent-Behavior-Consequence Model) is the foundation for understanding why people do what they do. Behavior is influenced by things that come before (Antecedents) and things that come after (Consequences).

2. Antecedents (for example, safety meetings, training, signs, instructions, policies and procedures) are important and necessary but by themselves won't lead to lasting behavior change.

3. Behavior is primarily influenced by consequences (e.g., praise, saving time, being comfortable, getting hurt, getting reprimanded).

4. Positive reinforcement (R+) is the most efficient and effective consequence and is the only one that has positive side effects.

5. A positive reinforcer is *anything* that makes behavior more likely (e.g., something that makes the job easier or more comfortable, peer approval, customer appreciation, getting the job done faster, and supervisor praise).

6. Negative reinforcement is when people work to avoid an undesired consequence ("do it or else"), and leads to just-enough-to-get-by performance.

7. Negative reinforcement and punishment (e.g., criticism, corrections, reprimands) are the most common consequences in safety and have negative side effects.

8. Immediate and certain consequences are the most powerful. Seemingly small consequences (saving a few minutes, being more comfortable) can be extremely powerful if they are immediate and certain. Seemingly large consequences (getting injured, earning an incentive) can be weak if they are in the future and/or are uncertain.

9. A 4:1 ratio of positive to negative consequences is ideal for producing optimal performance, building engagement, and maintaining a positive culture.

10. By positively reinforcing gradual improvement, consistent safe behavior can be shaped over time. Negative consequences are often unnecessary as safe behaviors replace unsafe behaviors.

11. It takes many reinforcers to create a habit.

CHAPTER 2

ENGAGE THE WORKFORCE

An engaged workforce is safer, more productive, and a pleasure to supervise.

Why This Matters

Achieving the ultimate goal of getting your team home safely *every day* requires more than just enforcing compliance with safety rules and regulations. You need an engaged team of employees who are willing to actively participate in safety.

Consider These Two Teams:

(1) Liz's team is quiet during start-up meetings. She does all the talking and sometimes wonders if her team is even

listening. She has begun having the meetings standing up on the shop floor because she found that when she had them sitting in the lunch room some of the guys fell asleep. She knows her team members are smart and they know their jobs well but she feels like she has to be "on them" all the time to make sure they are wearing their safety gear and following procedures. Whenever situations change, or they start a new task, she has to go out and make sure they do a new risk assessment like they are supposed to. Despite the training they recently attended on peer feedback, Liz's team members rarely give each other feedback about safe or at-risk behavior. When she asks about it, they say they just don't feel comfortable and they think it isn't their place. They don't report near misses, unless they are pretty serious, despite her urging them to do so. They do report hazards; however, Liz is frustrated that they could fix some of the hazards they report, but they don't.

(2) Juan's team actively participates in start-up meetings. Their discussions are lively and focused on the tasks they are about to do and how to keep each other safe. They ask questions, offer suggestions, and take the meetings seriously. Whenever situations change or they start a new task, Juan is confident they do a new risk assessment because they often tell him about it and sometimes ask for his assistance as a result of doing the assessment. After the recent training on peer feedback, they started giving each other feedback on safe and at-risk behavior. They tell Juan that they are not completely comfortable with it yet, but they are giving it an honest try and are starting to see the benefit. They report near misses and ask to participate in

the review of the near misses. They report hazards but usually just the major ones because they take care of the minor ones themselves.

Which team would you rather supervise? Clearly frontline employees who are engaged in safety are much easier to manage, and ultimately are much safer. It's tempting to say that Liz is just unlucky because she has a group of introverts, or a group that just doesn't care about safety. It is certainly true that there are individual differences within a workforce, but what you do as a supervisor can make a significant difference in how engaged your team is in safety.

Much has been written about the importance of engagement in creating a strong safety culture. But what specifically does engagement look like and why is it helpful?

An engaged workforce does the following:

Participates in safety discussions—Engaged employees actively participate in all discussions about safety and share their perspective. No one knows the challenges of performing the work safely better than the people who perform the work. Therefore, it is important that frontline employees talk about what gets in their way. Leadership's job is to make it as easy as possible for frontline employees to do their work safely. In order to do that, leaders need to know what the obstacles are. Active participation from the front line helps avoid the creation of "solutions" that won't work because they don't get at the true root causes.

Plans for and anticipates hazards—Today's workplaces are constantly changing so it is impossible for supervisors or safety personnel to anticipate and plan for every hazard.

Engaged employees are constantly scanning for hazards, thinking through their work thoroughly, anticipating what might go wrong, and planning carefully how to complete the work safely. When all eyes, ears, and brains are engaged, more hazards are identified and risk is minimized.

Actively works to keep peers safe—Engaged employees watch out for each other. They prompt each other around safety-critical tasks and give each other positive and constructive feedback on safety behaviors. The value of having your whole team watching and working to help each other develop safe habits is immeasurable. We all need feedback to stay safe. The more feedback we get, the safer we are. Supervisors simply don't have the time to do all of the observations and provide the frequent feedback that is required to help build safe habits. There is power in numbers.

Reports hazards—Engaged employees report hazards. Not just the physical hazards (e.g., an old piece of equipment that shows signs of failure) but behavioral and procedural hazards as well (e.g., decisions that have resulted in unanticipated risks or procedure changes that are causing dangerous shortcuts). Hearing about hazards and problems before they become incidents allows for truly preventative safety management.

Reports near misses—Engaged employees report near misses. Near misses provide rare opportunities to learn about what is not working as planned. Truly engaged employees go beyond "softball" events like close encounters with a wasp's nest and paper cuts. Any event that could have resulted in injury, illness, or damage is seen as a learning opportunity. The epitome of good reporting is when employees report near misses that are a function of their own at-risk behaviors in order to improve themselves and to shine a light on risks that others may well be taking.

Challenges decisions—Management makes decisions, often in the absence of all of the relevant information, particularly regarding safety. A new procedure, a new piece of equipment, a new vendor, may seem like a good idea to improve products, reduce waste, protect the environment, etc., but those making such decisions sometimes don't or can't thoroughly assess the impact on safety. Again, those who do the work are in the best position to do such assessments. Ideally they should be involved in the decision making up front, but that isn't always practical. An engaged workforce will challenge decisions or directions when they have safety concerns. This willingness to challenge can prevent minor and major safety issues. Too often after major incidents we hear of people who were there at the time who didn't speak up. "I didn't think that was safe, but I figured management knew what they were doing" is a phrase you never want to hear. When it comes to safety, it is everyone's job to question.

For these reasons and more, engagement is something worth investing in. If you have supervised a team for any period of time, you probably don't need to be convinced. You know that an engaged workforce makes your job as a

An engaged workforce makes your job as a supervisor easier.

supervisor easier and is an essential component of improving safety. The question is how to get it. All the steps in this book are designed to help you build engagement. But one tip is so essential to building engagement and improving safety that it is important to introduce it here. If you work on nothing else in this book, work on getting better at this—*increasing your use of positive reinforcement.*

You probably know that positive reinforcement is important when supervising people, but do you know why? The answer may surprise you. If you review the list of what an *engaged* workforce does, you will see a common thread—all of the behaviors are voluntary. They are not requirements of the job. Employees can choose to do them or not. It is common to hear management say, "Safety is a condition of working here," but an employee who works hard and follows safety rules but doesn't speak up at safety meetings, or doesn't report a lot of hazards, is not likely to be fired. A safe employee is not necessarily an engaged employee. Engagement behaviors are above and beyond the requirements of the job. They are discretionary. Like discretionary income that you can choose to spend or not, employees can choose to be engaged or not. The science of behavior has shown that the only way to get discretionary effort is through positive reinforcement.

> The only way to get discretionary effort is through positive reinforcement.

Unfortunately, most organizations don't set up their supervisors to manage safety with positive reinforcement.

They set up their supervisors to focus on the negative—what employees are doing wrong instead of right. Ask most frontline employees and they will tell you that they only hear from their supervisor around safety when they have done something wrong (engaged in at-risk behaviors, failed to follow a procedure, etc.). Not surprisingly, many supervisors see their role as enforcers of safety rules. The trouble with the safety enforcer approach is that it builds resentment.

Think about your team. What percent of the time are they working safely? Most supervisors will say 95 percent or higher. If your team is working safely 95 percent of the time and the only time they hear from you is the few times they are not, you can see how that might build resentment. We all want to feel appreciated. People don't expect constant praise for working safely, but it feels unfair to rarely, if ever, get acknowledgment for working safely the vast majority of the time. The bottom line is that when leaders pay more attention to what's wrong rather than what's right, resentment builds and engagement is undermined. So make sure you pay attention to what people are doing well. By paying attention to what you want, not just what you don't want, you'll get more of what you want and you'll get more engagement.

> Focus on what you WANT, not on what you DON'T WANT.

START TODAY!

You can start improving your safety leadership with this simple step—try to catch people in the act of doing things safely. When you walk through the work area, scan for what is right, instead of what is wrong. Look for people following safety procedures, using PPE properly, discussing hazards, helping each other out, etc., and then say something positive about what you see.

CHAPTER 3

BUILD RELATIONSHIPS

"People don't care how much you know, until they know how much you care." —Theodore Roosevelt

Why This Matters

Relationships are important in all aspects of life and business, and they are particularly important in safety. It's no coincidence that supervisors who have strong relationships with their crews tend to have safer crews. Working on developing good relationships helps with safety in three ways: (1) by building trust, (2) by increasing reinforcement effectiveness, and (3) by demonstrating care and concern.

Building Trust

Trust is important in safety because it is a key ingredient in engagement. If you think about it, engagement is risky business for frontline employees. Giving constructive feedback to a peer, stopping a job because it isn't safe, challenging a decision—these are risky. Not the kind of risks that might lead to injuries—the kind that might lead to other negative consequences such as getting in trouble, flak from peers, getting a reputation for being difficult, not getting promoted, and so on. Most of us take risks only when we trust the person we are taking a risk with or for. We must trust that they understand our good intentions; we must trust that they won't react negatively; we must trust they won't use our words or actions against us.

So, part of your job as a supervisor is to develop relationships with your direct reports so that they trust you enough to stop a job, challenge a decision, and tell you about unsafe events, without fear of repercussion. Your goal should be to build trust to the point that each of your direct reports would be comfortable coming to you and saying, "I just messed up," or "I took a safety shortcut and here is why," or "I just had a serious near miss because of something I did." These are difficult words to say when the person you are saying them to has the power to have you fired. But until you reach that point, you won't fully know what all the risks and hazards are in your work area, and if you don't know about risks, you can't effectively manage them. Chapter 7 will cover the important topic of how you respond to such admissions without seeming to be too soft on safety, or failing to hold people accountable. It can be done while still building the trust that is essential for being as informed as possible about all of the risks and temptations in the workplace.

Building trust is not easy but the recipe for trust is simple—do what you say you will do. If you say you are going to get back to someone with an answer to a question, get back to them. If you say you are going to get your team a new

Build trust by doing what you say you will do.

tool, get the new tool. If you say you are going to get the soda machine fixed, get it fixed. Every time you do what you say you will do, you build trust. Every time you fail to do what you say you will do, you erode trust; every time. And it doesn't matter why you didn't do it—you forgot, you sent an email to someone about it and they never got back to you, the item was out of stock, your boss pulled you away to another meeting. You may know that you have good reasons for not following through but if your direct reports don't know your good reasons they will assume that you just didn't bother, you never intended to do it, or worst of all—you lied. If you can't do what you said you would do, then tell your team why you can't. If they ask for something and the answer is "no," then tell them so and tell them why. You will get credit for trying and for following up with them.

Increasing Reinforcement Effectiveness

Relationships are also important because they influence your ability to use positive reinforcement effectively. As noted, one of the most important things you can do as a supervisor is to positively reinforce critical safety behaviors. Not only does this make common sense ("You attract more flies with honey than vinegar"), it is a scientific fact that positive reinforcement is the most effective way to improve performance of any kind. While most supervisors intuitively know this, it's hard to break out of the role of *safety cop.* But this is one change that is essential to improve safety. Safety cops don't tend to have good relationships with the people they are policing. Think of it from your team's perspective: it's hard to have a good relationship with someone who is always pointing out what you are doing wrong. Just ask most teenagers. The teenage years are the most trying in parent-child relationships partly because parents spend a disproportionate amount of time telling teenagers what they didn't do ("You didn't make your bed," "You haven't mowed the lawn," "I told you to take out the garbage") and what they did wrong ("I can't believe you lost your homework again," "When will you learn to turn off the lights when you leave a room?" "If you don't study harder you'll never get into college").

Negativity erodes relationships, even when it is used to be helpful. When relationships are poor, positive reinforcement is less effective. A positive comment like, "Thanks for taking care of that hazard," is not likely to be reinforcing if the receiver resents the person who says it. Said more plainly, it's hard to positively reinforce someone who dislikes you. Positive reinforcement is often about telling people you appreciate them or are impressed with what they have done. If the person dislikes you, they are not likely to care if you are grateful or impressed, and they certainly are not motivated to continue to do things that make you happy.

So, good relationships make your delivery of positive reinforcement more effective because people care what you think. Ironically, one of the ways to build better relationships is by using more positive reinforcement, but it has to be done in conjunction with other relationship-building activities (see *Tips for Building Effective Relationships*).

> Positive reinforcement improves relationships and relationships improve positive reinforcement.

Demonstrating Care and Concern

Finally, relationships matter in safety because of how our behavior changes when we genuinely care about the people around us. If you have children, you have experienced this. Within hours of the birth of my first child I was struck by one sudden and certain realization, that I would do anything to protect my son—anything. We are all hardwired to protect the people we care about. This shows up in sometimes dramatic ways (running into a burning building to save someone you care about) but more often in many subtle ways (spending a little extra time explaining a safety rule, and providing recognition when it gets followed). So, caring more about the people who work for you will change your behavior in subtle and not-so-subtle ways that will have a positive impact on safety. As you build stronger relationships, you inevitably start to care more. In turn, the fact that your direct reports know you are emotionally invested in them, rather than viewing them as a pair of hands to get the job done, will make them want to behave in ways that please you.

Making It Happen

By now I hope you are convinced (if you weren't already) that relationships are important in safety. Developing good relationships will help you build trust, will enable the use of positive reinforcement, and will change your leadership behaviors in helpful ways.

So, how do you go about building better relationships at work? Developing relationships is easy for some people and more difficult for others. One of the challenges of managing a team of people is that each team member is unique. You may have some individuals who are easy to relate to and with whom you have easily developed respectful, productive relationships. You may have others with whom developing relationships is more challenging. The tips that follow will help supervisors, young or old, inexperienced or veteran. Remember, your job as a supervisor is to support the people who report to you so that they can do their jobs as safely and productively as possible. Building relationships will set the groundwork for supporting the people who work for you.

Tips for Building Effective Relationships

1. **Treat direct reports like people, not just employees.** Make a point to get to know direct reports. Greet them at the start of the shift; show an interest in their lives outside of work, and demonstrate concern and consideration.

2. **Set clear expectations.** Pinpoint your expectations to make sure they are clear. Avoid assumptions and ask direct reports to state their understanding of the expectations if there is any chance of confusion.

3. **Acknowledge good work, not just mistakes/problems.** Keep track of how many of your interactions are positive (recognizing desired behavior) versus corrective or constructive (discussing mistakes, at-risk behaviors, etc.) and work towards maintaining a higher ratio of positive to constructive comments/discussions.

4. **Ask questions to understand problems/issues.** Avoid jumping to conclusions. Avoid blame. There is always more to every story, so ask questions to uncover the details.

5. **Listen.** Use active listening skills such as maintaining eye contact, using appropriate facial expressions, paraphrasing, and asking questions to demonstrate understanding. Avoid looking at or using computers and smart phones when others are talking to you.

6. **Admit when you make mistakes.** Acknowledging your own mistakes helps establish that mistakes are expected and that learning from them is critical.

7. **Solicit input and opinions from direct reports.** Asking for input and advice (and acting on it) will not only lead to better solutions, but it can also demonstrate respect. It shows that you value their expertise.

8. **Follow through on commitments.** Use whatever memory devices you need to be sure to do what you say you will do (e.g., hand-written sticky notes, reminders in your smart phone). And if you can't, explain why you can't. Consistent follow-through is essential for building trust.

START TODAY!

Pick one or two items from the list above and set a target to work on those items each day. If you are a new supervisor, start with #1. Once you are in the habit of greeting everyone and you have learned a little bit about them, select another item from the list and work on that. If you are a seasoned supervisor and you have good relationships with your direct reports, you might start with #7 and get some input from them on areas for improvement. No matter what stage you are in, set small, achievable goals based on the best practices above, and look for the impact on engagement and your ability to have a positive influence. A few minutes a day will lead to big payoffs.

CHAPTER 4

BE RELENTLESS ABOUT FIXING HAZARDS

"Unless someone like you cares a whole awful lot, nothing is going to get better. It's not."—Dr. Seuss

Why This Matters

Below are some all-too-common complaints heard from frontline employees.

- "I reported that hazard twice and they still haven't fixed it."
- "They say they fixed it but they just patched it up with duct tape. It will fall apart again in a few weeks."
- "They have known about this problem for four months and they are just now getting around to solving it."

- "The only time they fix things is after someone gets hurt."
- "If it costs money, they won't fix it."
- "They fix the big stuff right away, but there are all kinds of smaller hazards that never get fixed."

Frontline employees gauge how truly important safety is in an organization by management's willingness to invest in keeping the workplace as free of hazards as possible. Right or wrong, hazard remediation is the litmus test. It's not what leaders say about safety, it's not the quality of safety training, it's not the frequency of safety meetings—it's whether or not management takes care of hazards. In organizations where the perception is that management does not take care of hazards, it is common to hear statements like this:

> Hazard Remediation is the litmus test for management's commitment to safety.

- "They give us a hard time about not participating in safety meetings but it's a joke—they won't fix the unsafe conditions we tell them about, so why should we participate?"
- "They want us to do stretching before shifts and the guys just roll their eyes. It's hard to get excited about stretching when the tools we are using are falling apart and the guards on half the machines are broken."

When management doesn't take care of hazards, employees are less likely to do more than the bare minimum. When management does a good job of taking care of hazards, employees are willing to participate more fully in safety. It's basic reciprocity—if you do your part, I'll do mine. From the front line's perspective, fixing hazards is "your part."

While management's role in safety goes beyond addressing hazards, hazards are tangible. Your crew is reminded every day if you fail to fix a rickety handrail, or fail to replace a faulty guard on a saw. These unsafe conditions provide a visible way for frontline employees to gauge your commitment to safety. By taking care of hazards, you go beyond the words "safety is important"—you *demonstrate* that it is important. You demonstrate that the people who work for you are important. That is why it is essential to be relentless about fixing hazards—it is the yardstick by which your team will measure your commitment to safety and, by extension, your commitment to them.

> By taking care of hazards you demonstrate the importance of safety.

Obviously, as a frontline supervisor, you don't have complete control over addressing every hazard identified. Many hazard fixes cost money; some require taking production off-line, and some require resources from other departments. The good news is that most frontline employees understand these limitations. They don't expect you to be able to replace an expensive piece of equipment because it leaks oil, or to shut down production every time they report a hazard. What they do expect (and need) is a good-faith effort and lots of communication.

A Note about the Hierarchy of Safety Control

Before getting into some tips for hazard remediation, it's important to discuss the hierarchy of safety control. If you aren't familiar with it, the hierarchy of safety control outlines five ways to control hazards. Importantly, the five methods are prioritized according to effectiveness. Supervisors should always work at the highest level possible. *Elimination* (removing the hazard) and *Substitution* (replacing hazardous products or procedures) are at the top of the hierarchy because they provide the best protection. *Engineering Controls* are next in the hierarchy and involve trying to remove a hazard or put a barrier between the employees and the hazard. *Administrative Controls* (implementing training procedures and policies) and *Personal Protective Equipment* are considered the least effective, but necessary, where hazards cannot be controlled via other means.

Be sure to use the hierarchy of control when addressing hazards. Obviously, completely getting rid of hazards is the best solution. If the hazard is gone, no one can get hurt. Controls on the lower part of the hierarchy are less effective precisely because, rather than removing the hazard, they include changing the behavior of people in the workplace to avoid or minimize the hazard. It's much harder to sustain behavioral solutions than physical solutions.

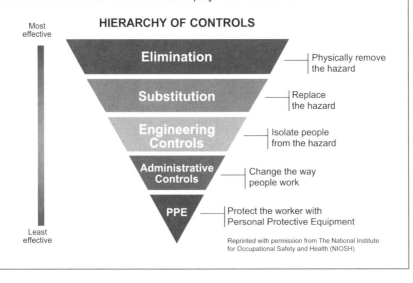

HIERARCHY OF CONTROLS

Most effective

Elimination — Physically remove the hazard

Substitution — Replace the hazard

Engineering Controls — Isolate people from the hazard

Administrative Controls — Change the way people work

PPE — Protect the worker with Personal Protective Equipment

Least effective

Reprinted with permission from The National Institute for Occupational Safety and Health (NIOSH)

Hazard Remediation Systems

In a perfect world, workplaces would be designed safely from the outset—all hazards would be engineered out of the environment before employees ever arrive. Unfortunately, very few people work in startup facilities, and even brand new, state-of-the-art facilities are rarely perfect. Most of you are working in facilities that are not ideally designed from a safety perspective. Perhaps your workplace is old, doesn't have enough space, or is outside where Mother Nature is in charge of the design and the conditions. Your challenge as a supervisor is to make the environment your team currently works in as safe as possible. Short of redesigning the work environment, this is done largely through hazard identification and remediation systems.

Every organization has such a system. Some are very formal and elaborate and some are very informal. While there are ways to make the actual systems better (see the book *Safe by Accident* for suggestions), you may not have a say in how the hazard remediation system is handled in your organization. Following is a list of some things you can do regardless of your organization's system.

How to be Relentless About Fixing Hazards

Fix hazards quickly. This goes without saying, but I'm saying it anyway. For the hazards within your control, the sooner you fix them the better. It reduces risk in the workplace and it increases engagement (and trust). Just do it!

Ask about hazards frequently. There are hazards in

every workplace but only some of them get reported. Sometimes people notice them but neglect to report them, and sometimes people don't even see them. By asking about hazards frequently (daily or weekly), you help train people to look for hazards and you give them lots of opportunities to report them. Avoid general questions like, "Have you seen any hazards today?" Ask questions that help them know where to look for possible hazards. Some examples include the following:

- Is there anything in the work area that concerns you from a safety perspective?
- Is all of the equipment working okay?
- Has anything changed that might have introduced a hazard?
- When you started this new task, what did you talk about when you assessed the hazards?
- Is there anything that is making you nervous?

Make reporting easy. Most hazard identification systems require too much effort or hassle to report a hazard. If hourly employees have to fill out even a little paperwork to report hazards, they are less likely to report. Even when there are opportunities to report hazards verbally during meetings, not all hazards will get reported. Recently a frontline employee told me that his supervisor asks about hazards at every morning start-up meeting. Sounds ideal, right? In fact, the employee said that he and most of the other crew members aren't fully awake at these 5 a.m. meetings, and they often don't remember the hazards from the previous day, so very few hazards get reported.

To truly capture all hazards, employees need to be able to report hazards as they see them or as they appear without having to go somewhere and fill out a form, remember them for the next safety meeting, or wait for a formal inspection. The easiest way for frontline employees to report hazards is to tell their supervisor when the supervisor is out in the work area. Unfortunately, most frontline supervisors I know are juggling dozens of things at a time so it is easy to forget about a hazard someone mentioned in passing. My advice is to write down all hazards immediately when they are reported to you. Make a note in your smart phone or carry a small pad of paper in your pocket. Relying on your memory is too risky for this important task.

Encourage DIY fixes. Encourage your direct reports to deal with hazards themselves when possible. Many hazards should be left for maintenance professionals or engineers. However, frontline employees that take ownership around fixing hazards within their control often get more engaged in other parts of safety. Sometimes frontline employees just need permission—they need to know it is okay to do it themselves. Ultimately, you want a work team that does as much around safety as they can, and this is a great place to start.

Take personal responsibility. Even if someone else is technically accountable for fixing hazards, you should take personal responsibility for the hazards in your work area. This is one situation where you should never say, "Not my job." A hazard, no matter how small, is a risk to your team and their personal safety is your responsibility; therefore, it is your job. You may not do all of the legwork like entering the hazards into a tracking system, ordering parts, etc., but you should shepherd the hazards through to resolution. In other words, you should make sure it happens.

Create a feedback loop. Keep a running record of the hazards that have been reported and communicate status frequently. Posting the list of reported hazards on the wall in the work area when possible adds accountability for fixing the hazards. It prompts you (and others) to check on hazards that are still outstanding. Be sure to include the date reported, status, priority, and projected date of resolution. If posting the list isn't possible (it can be a liability issue), communicate verbally the status of reported hazards at least once a week. Make a habit of talking about hazards during daily or weekly meetings. You cannot overcommunicate around hazards.

Discuss priorities. Since resources are always limited, hazards are often prioritized. This is most often done through maintenance work-order systems and capital-request processes. Work orders and capital requests that are safety related are usually given priority over non-safety ones, but are still prioritized. Not everything can get fixed right away. It is important to inform the people who report a hazard of the priority and the reason for the priority assigned, particularly if a hazard gets a low priority or is not going to get addressed at all. It's better to be honest about what is going to happen and when, rather than leave people wondering.

Ask for input on fixes. The people who work around a hazard are often in the best position to suggest how it can be fixed. By asking for their input you will often arrive at better solutions and you will build engagement.

Escalate when necessary. As a frontline supervisor, you won't have the resources to deal with all hazards. While you can't run to your boss requesting money for every hazard reported, you do need to know when it is time to take a hazard to the next level of management for more immediate action. It may be due to the severity of the hazard or the level of concern your team has about it. Gently reminding your boss that hazard remediation is the litmus test for management's commitment to safety may help. Even if your boss can't approve a fix, perhaps he or she can come and talk to your team about why, and let them express their concern. Remember, communication about hazards can be as important as fixing them.

To summarize, here are some ways you can be relentless about fixing hazards:

- Fix hazards quickly.
- Ask about hazards frequently.
- Make reporting easy.
- Encourage DIY fixes, when appropriate.
- Take personal responsibility.
- Create a feedback loop.
- Discuss priorities.
- Ask for input on fixes.
- Escalate when necessary.

START TODAY!

From the list on the previous page, select one or two things that you can improve upon today. Perhaps you can walk around and ask your team about hazards. Maybe you can address a hazard that is low priority from a safety perspective, but a high priority to your crew. Perhaps you can post the hazard list with dates of estimated fixes. These are great ways to demonstrate you care about safety and build the reciprocity required for engagement.

CHAPTER 5

CONCENTRATE ON BEHAVIORS THAT MATTER

"Don't lead by results; lead to results. Only behavior will get you there."—Aubrey Daniels

Why This Matters

In addition to being responsible for keeping the workplace as free of hazards as possible, supervisors are also responsible for ensuring that frontline employees behave safely. It's your job to ensure your direct reports do everything they learned in training, follow all the safety rules, and comply with policies and procedures. Wouldn't it be great if you could just train them, show them procedures, tell them what to do, and they would do it all consistently and habitually? Unfortunately, that doesn't happen. The fact that it doesn't happen is predictable—you know it based on your personal experience. And the science of behavior predicts it as well. In scientific terms, training, rules, policies, procedures, instructions, and safety signage are all called antecedents. Antecedents are things that come before behavior that prompt behavior. Training prompts people to do things. Instructions prompt people to do things. Signs prompt people to do things. What we know from the science (and what you know from your experience) is that the effects of antecedents are short-lived, at best. You might review a new procedure during a team meeting and then immediately see people following the new procedure. A few weeks later you are likely to notice that most people have gone back to the old procedure. Why is this so? Because the new procedure wasn't reinforced in the workplace, and old habits die hard. If the new procedure is difficult, time-consuming, or just tough because it is new and different from the old way, then the temptation is to revert to familiar, easier, faster ways of doing things. Often this is not a conscious decision. People just slip back into the old, comfortable ways.

Because of this fact of human nature, part of your job as a supervisor is to observe your team working and ensure they engage in required safety behaviors. You do this through formal inspections, but more frequently through informal observations, when you are in the work area. Observations lead to conversations about safe and at-risk behavior. What you say and do during these conversations will have a bigger influence on your team members' behavior than will any of the antecedents you might use.

Your feedback, approval, disappointment, appreciation, frustration, etc. are all behavioral consequences, which are the supervisor's primary tools for influencing behavior.

> Antecedents get behavior started, consequences keep them going.

Most supervisors do informal observations without a plan. They look around while walking through an area and "see what they see." In my experience, what supervisors tend to "see" falls into two categories. The first is the easy-to-observe stuff. PPE is at the top of this list. You don't even have to stop walking to know whether someone is wearing glasses, gloves, hats, and ear plugs. These are also easy behaviors to give feedback on. The clear-cut nature of PPE makes feedback conversations easy—no disagreeing about whether someone is or should be wearing a hard hat or safety glasses. The second category is "top of mind" stuff like behaviors related to a recent injury (someone just had a hand injury so you are looking at pinch points), or a boss's hot button (she is a stickler about housekeeping so you focus on that). Think about your work environment. If you could only give feedback on two or three behaviors (in order to improve them over time), what would they be? Would you choose PPE or those hot-button issues? Are those the behaviors that will protect your crew from the most frequent injuries and the most catastrophic ones?

Ideally you would observe and give systematic feedback on all safety-related behaviors. Unfortunately, that isn't realistic—there are too many behaviors and you have limited time. Feedback is a powerful tool and a precious resource. You must use this limited resource deliberately and wisely. Most supervisors spread their feedback across so many safety behaviors that improvement on any one behavior is slow at best. By giving focused attention to the most critical behaviors, significant improvements can be achieved, and injuries avoided. Over time you can work through a longer list, but just focus on a few at any one point in time.

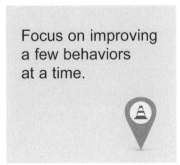

Focus on improving a few behaviors at a time.

So how do you decide what the most critical behaviors are? An obvious strategy is to focus on those behaviors that are causing the most frequent incidents in your work area, your organization, or your industry. This is a great place to start; however, there is a danger in limiting your focus to only those behaviors.

Preventing Serious Incidents

Recently, attention has been paid to the fact that while rates of less-serious incidents have declined greatly in the last two decades, there has been a much slower decline in serious injuries and fatalities (SIFs). In other words, we are reducing strains, sprains, cuts, and contusions, but people are still being seriously injured and killed on the job at rates not much better than those of 20 years ago. Clearly, we need to adjust our strategies to achieve reductions in serious and fatal injuries as well as more minor ones.

A number of factors have contributed to this failure to significantly reduce SIFs. One big contributor is the heavy focus on reducing incident rate, including the popularity of having a goal of zero. As organizations get closer to zero injuries they sometimes spend a disproportionate amount of time and resources on minor injuries that tend to happen more frequently (e.g., slips and trips, minor hand injuries). These high-frequency, low-severity incidents get a great deal of attention as people attempt to eliminate those last few incidents and improve their rate. In doing so, less attention may be paid to preventing incidents that don't happen very often, but when they do they are major (e.g., explosions, chemical releases, falls from height). Organizations can and do go many years without having one of these serious events, so their impact on annually calculated incident rates can be minimal—the result being they get less attention than they deserve.

We have all heard stories of organizations that went many years without a lost-time incident only to have a very serious or fatal incident. In many cases, the warning signs were there, but everyone was focused on ice in the parking lot and preventing bee stings. While it makes sense to focus on things that hurt your employees most often, don't lose sight of the injuries that are really unlikely to happen, but if they did, would be catastrophic. Often the prevention of SIFs has more to do with management systems (and thus management behavior) than frontline behavior; however, all root causes should be assessed.

The bottom line is, when deciding what frontline behaviors are worthy of systematic feedback, include both those that prevent frequent, minor injuries and those that prevent more serious ones. Here are some strategies for each category.

Targeting High-Frequency, Low-Severity Behaviors

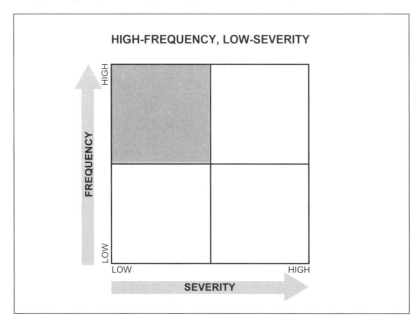

If your organization has a significant number of injuries, or if you have access to industry incident data, you can analyze those data to identify important behaviors to focus on. For example, many organizations have a large number of slips, trips, and falls. Some underlying behaviors might include holding handrails when using stairs, maintaining three points of contact when climbing on and off equipment, rolling up hoses after use, and keeping eyes on path. Strains and sprains are another common category of injury. Underlying behaviors might include bending and lifting with back straight and knees bent, using lifting devices, and using the proper tool for the job. Improving the consistency of these behaviors will reduce injuries (both minor and potentially serious) and are worth focusing on.

If your organization doesn't have many incidents (and thus you can't look at incident data to determine behaviors to focus on), use near miss reports if you have them. In the absence of both incident data and near miss data, you will have to rely on observation and analysis of your team's current safe and at-risk behaviors. Just go watch your crew work for an extended period of time and you are likely to see inconsistent safe behaviors. Asking employees for input is another excellent way to identify critical behaviors. If you have a good relationship with your crew, they will tell you which safety behaviors need improvement.

Targeting Low-Frequency, High-Severity Behaviors

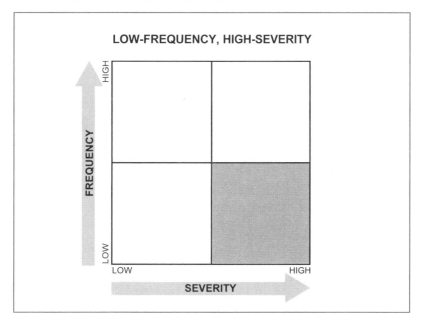

As previously noted, one of the reasons we don't pay enough attention to behaviors that contribute to serious injuries is that (thankfully) most organizations don't have that many of them. While that is a good thing, it also makes it difficult to figure out what behaviors a frontline supervisor should pay attention to in preventing these serious events. There is some excellent research on the causes of SIFs (see Martin & Black, Sept. 2015). My goal is not to review this interesting topic, but to point you toward some activities and situations that are worthy of your attention as a frontline supervisor.

As you might have guessed, serious injuries and fatalities occur most often when employees are engaged in high-risk activities so that is a good place to start. Martin and Black state that 42 percent of SIFs in their study were associated with the following activities:

- Lockout/tagout
- Confined space entry
- Working at elevations
- Machine guarding/barricades
- Operations of mobile equipment
- Suspended loads
- Equipment and pipe openings
- Hot-work permits
- Excavations and trenches
- Arc flash protection

While there might be a number of things a supervisor should do to reduce the chance of SIFs during these activities (for example, assessing effectiveness of training, ensuring thorough pre-task risk assessments, and evaluating Standard Operating Procedures), one thing is clear—

observations done during these high-risk activities are necessary. Because of the dangerous nature of these activities it is essential that you go out and observe to see that procedures are being followed precisely, 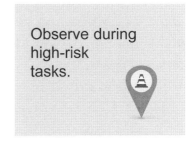 and that all important safe behaviors take place. The more you are able to observe, the more just-in-time feedback you can provide to help ensure that the right things happen.

Another situation in which serious injuries and fatalities occur is during routine tasks when a change occurs that increases risk. My colleague, Cloyd Hyten, refers to these as "emerging hazards" and notes, importantly, that often many organizations do pre-task risk assessments and these emerging hazards are not discussed. Thus, a pre-task assessment should include a thorough assessment of the task and the hazards associated with the task, as well as a discussion of what might change in the environment that would change the risk (the emerging hazards). Examples are a tool wearing out, power interruption, fatigue setting in (if the task is long), change in weather, or increasing pressure from others who might be waiting on the task to be completed. While it is impossible to think of every possible scenario, it is important to ensure that pre-task assessments include "what if" questions and a plan for additional just-in-time task assessments if situations change significantly. While many organizations train employees to do these important behaviors (pre-task assessments, mid-task assessments if something changes, "what if" questions), it is up to you as a supervisor to not only ensure they are completed by your direct reports, but also to help them continuously improve. These are not simple behaviors but by working together you can help your team get better over time.

Planning Observations

As you have undoubtedly realized, observing and giving feedback on truly critical behaviors requires planning. You aren't likely to see many of the critical behaviors you have identified when you walk through the work area on your way to a meeting. These behaviors often require that you think about when and where they can be observed and then schedule time on your calendar to observe. Make a habit of blocking time each week to ensure that this important safety leadership behavior happens.

The Importance of Being Specific

As mentioned, some behaviors are easy to observe and give feedback on. For example, you either have a reflective vest on or you don't; you either engaged the machine guard or you did not. Other important safety behaviors are not so clear-cut. For example, the quality of "what if" questions asked during a pre-task assessment is not a clear-cut behavior. Thus, once you have identified critical behaviors to focus on, it is important to define or pinpoint those behaviors as specifically as possible. If employees are unclear as to the safe behavior required,

Pinpoint critical safe behaviors.

then the likelihood of them doing the right thing is lower and thus the risk is higher. Never assume your team knows what you mean or that they know what to do because they are experienced. Too often, supervisors discover that they weren't clear only after an incident occurs. A dramatic example occurred a number of years ago with one of our mining clients. Underground mines have very large, heavy transport vehicles (to move people and equipment) that run on tracks. These vehicles are secured by chaining them to the tracks. In this instance a supervisor told a crew member to check to make sure the vehicle was secure (chained to the track at one end) because he was going to unchain the other end. The employee did a visual check from a distance of about 10 feet and reported that the chain was attached. It was not. When the supervisor disconnected the vehicle from the other end, the vehicle rolled, unmanned, a long distance into the mine and finally derailed. It was an extremely dangerous event, but luckily no one was injured. This incident was caused by a lack of pinpointing. The supervisor told the employee to *check* but didn't pinpoint *how* to check. Others knew to check manually by using a hand or foot to ensure there was tension on the chain, but not everyone knew to do that and the supervisor didn't specify that in his instructions.

A good starting point for pinpointing is to describe only observable behaviors—behaviors you can see or hear. You can see someone tying off before working at height. You cannot see someone being "aware of his surroundings" when working at height. The litmus test for pinpointing is that if three people simultaneously observed the target behavior for a period of time, would all three have the same count of how many times that

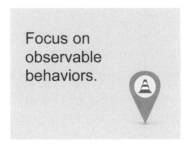

Focus on observable behaviors.

behavior occurred? If not, the behavior needs to be pinpointed further. This is more complicated than it seems. For example, "keep hands away from pinch points" sounds well pinpointed, but how far away is *away*—five inches, ten inches? This lack of clarity can get people hurt. Pinpointing may seem unnecessary or excessive but it is actually a life-saving communication tool.

Pinpointing "Pay Attention"

"If they would pay more attention to what they were doing, incidents wouldn't happen!" How many times have you heard this? *Paying attention* seems like the holy grail of safety behaviors in that it appears it would prevent many incidents. The problem is this: paying attention isn't an observable behavior.

Sometimes we can pinpoint behaviors that equate to *paying attention.* Examples include—look where you step, turn off electronic devices before driving, and check mirrors every five seconds. Sometimes we can't pinpoint one behavior that gets at paying attention because the tasks we are interested in vary greatly, or, paying attention isn't manifested in some physical behavior. L. David Marquet, in his excellent book *Turn the Ship Around!* describes how he and the crew of the nuclear-powered submarine he was in command of figured out a way to help people pay attention and not make mistakes during critical tasks. They came up with a procedure they called "Take Deliberate Action." The procedure was used prior to any critical action and involved the operator pausing, gesturing, and vocalizing what he/she was about to do. For example, an operator would pause, point to a lever and say, "I'm going to turn this lever one-quarter turn to the left." The idea came from an incident investigation when someone stated that the operator involved in the incident wasn't paying attention. He was "on autopilot." Take Deliberate Action was a way to behavioralize "Pay attention to what you are doing." It wasn't intended to make paying attention observable, although it does do that. It was meant to help the operators really focus on the task—where they were putting their hands and what specifically they were doing.

If your work area has critical tasks that require full attention but are in danger of being done on *autopilot,* then you might try getting your team to use this technique. You or others can then observe it and give feedback. If you can't be there to observe it, you can have a conversation with the employee after the task is complete and have him talk to you about what he did and how it went.

Tips for Focusing on Behaviors that Matter

Focusing your feedback on the most important behaviors will help you use this powerful resource to truly impact safety. Here is a summary of the tips from this chapter:

1. Antecedents (training, procedures, meetings, rules) have limited effect. Use feedback and recognition (positive consequences) to develop consistent safe behaviors.

2. Focus on a few behaviors at a time. You can't fix everything all at once. Identify a few critical behaviors to focus on, and move on to other behaviors once the initial ones have improved.

3. Observe high-frequency, low-severity and low-frequency, high-severity behaviors. Those frequent, minor injuries are important, but don't ignore the infrequent, big, bad stuff.

4. Use data to identify critical behaviors when possible (incident data, near miss data, or observational data).

5. Plan your observations in order to see critical behaviors. Be sure to do observations during high-risk activities to prevent serious injuries and fatalities.

6. Help employees look for and plan for emerging hazards.

7. Pinpoint critical safe behaviors so you and your team are absolutely clear on what those behaviors are.

Martin & Black (Sept 2015). Preventing Serious Injuries & Fatalities. *Professional Safety.*

Marquet, L. David (2012). *Turn the Ship Around! A True Story of Turning Followers into Leaders.* New York: Portfolio/Penguin.

CHAPTER 6

FOCUS ON WHAT YOU WANT (NOT ON WHAT YOU DON'T WANT)

"Never underestimate the power of positive reinforcement." —Aubrey Daniels

Why This Matters

Consider this scenario:

Matt is a mechanic in a manufacturing facility and has recently been assigned to a new area. He is a good mechanic, a helpful teammate, and is active on the department safety committee. One day his supervisor, Dean, notices him doing some Preventative Maintenance (PM) on one of the more finicky machines. He is clearly concentrating hard since this is his first round of PM on this machine. Dean is pleased to see he has followed the complicated lockout/tagout procedure properly and is wearing all of the correct PPE. While Dean is observing, Matt picks up a tool that is not the right tool for what he is doing. He starts to use the tool and Dean intervenes. He is clearly frustrated and says, "Matt, we just talked about this last week in our safety meeting. You are using the wrong tool for the job. You could get hurt, not to mention damage the tool or the machine. Please go get the correct tool." Matt gives Dean a confused look and starts to ask a question, but just then Dean's radio goes off and he leaves. The following week Matt resigns from the safety committee.

Countless safety interactions like the one above happen every day. When it is written in black and white it is easy to see the mistakes the supervisor made—neglecting to positively reinforce the safe behaviors, talking only about the at-risk behavior, failing to ask why or let the mechanic ask for clarification, reprimanding instead of coaching—and yet many well-intended supervisors make these mistakes over and over again. Why is this so?

It starts with how supervisors view their role in safety: safety cop or safety coach, enforcer or reinforcer? Underlying assumptions about your role in safety matter a great deal.

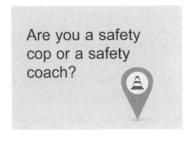

Are you a safety cop or a safety coach?

Think about what cops do. They look for people failing to follow rules. They scan for what's wrong. They view themselves as enforcers of the law so they seek violations. If you view yourself as a safety cop, as an enforcer of safety rules, it will influence what you see. You will see problems, violations, and things to be corrected. And what you see will determine how you respond. A focus on violations, problems, and at-risk behaviors leads to the use of corrective feedback at best, and more negative consequences (like discipline), at worst. Let me be clear, I'm not suggesting that you ignore at-risk behaviors. I am suggesting that what you attend to most sets in motion management practices that can be productive or destructive over the long run.

If you see yourself as a coach—as a reinforcer—then you look for what people are doing well, for what is right, and for ways to help people get even better. Again, what you look for determines what you see and what you see determines how you respond. A focus on what people are doing well leads to positive feedback and reinforcement. A focus on how you can help leads to positive coaching conversations rather than criticism and discipline.

Consider who is more effective at motivating people to do the right thing—a good sports coach or a police officer? A good coach brings out the best in people. A good coach inspires discretionary effort.

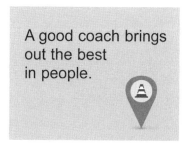

A good coach brings out the best in people.

A good coach is someone people seek out to help them improve. A police officer is someone people avoid (under most circumstances) because they tell people what they can't do, issue tickets, and in general provide negative consequences. Which would you rather be?

Why Are So Many Supervisors Safety Cops?

Most people agree that a positive coaching approach is better, so why isn't that the most common style of managing safety? As discussed, supervisors don't have time to talk to direct reports about every behavior they see. Therefore, many supervisors choose to manage the exceptions. Since most people work safely most of the time, it seems more efficient to only talk to people when at-risk behaviors (exceptions) are observed. While it is certainly less time-consuming, exception management has some undesirable side effects and does little to build safe habits (let alone engagement).

There is another reason so many well-intended supervisors end up being cops instead of coaches. It has to do with positional power and the default consequences associated with being a boss. When you are a boss, you can always rely on negative consequences to get people to do what you want or need. The bottom line is that you can reprimand, discipline, and even have someone fired if they don't do what you tell them to do. In reality most supervisors rarely use these options; however, employees understand that such negative consequences are always a possibility. Many supervisors (and managers) inadvertently rely on those *implied* threats. Relying on implied or explicit threats to motivate is called *negative reinforcement.* It is more commonly known as the "do it, or else" approach. This is the approach being used with statements like, "Safety is a condition of working here." The implication is if you don't work safely, you won't work here. Do it, or else. Unfortunately, this is the default approach to managing safety. Because negative reinforcement is *built-in* when you are the boss, asking or telling direct reports to do something comes with an implied "or else." If you don't deliberately use positive reinforcement to recognize desired behaviors, direct reports will do those behaviors only to avoid the "or else." Even very nice people end up using negative reinforcement, usually without realizing it.

For example, I recently worked with a supervisor who was very concerned about the safety of his crew. He had witnessed someone get seriously injured on the job and never wanted that to happen to anyone working for him. He believed he needed to be tough on safety. He made it clear to his crew that he took even minor safety violations very seriously. He told them he "wouldn't put up with" at-risk behaviors and that he had "high expectations" for all of them around safety. He asked that they "not disappoint" him. While his intentions were good, he inadvertently created an environment of fear in which his direct reports never reported near misses, hid mistakes, and failed to report minor injuries. Ironically, the best way to be tough on safety is not with threats and negative consequences, but with more consistent use of positive ones.

> The way to be tough on safety is to consistently use positive reinforcement for important behaviors.

Now, let me be clear, there are certainly circumstances in which supervisors need to use negative consequences (e.g., willful violations of safety rules, chronic offenders);

however, overreliance on this approach is problematic in several ways. First, it results in *just-enough-to-get-by performance.* In other words, people do only as much as they have to in order to avoid the negative consequences. In safety this often shows up as employees who follow procedures, do hazard assessments, and wear safety gear when the supervisor is watching, but not when supervision is absent. If you feel like you have to watch your crew all the time to ensure they work safely, you are probably unknowingly relying on the do-it-or-else approach. Don't feel bad; many supervisors and managers do the same and since you are reading this book, you are now learning a better way.

The second reason the do-it-or-else approach is problematic is that it has negative side effects. Negative reinforcement is fear-based motivation. Direct reports do what we ask out of fear of what will happen if they don't. Many people think that fear is the best motivator, and fear certainly can motivate. If we are fearful enough we will do what we need to do to escape or avoid what we are afraid of. The problem is that fear-based motivation, coupled with a lack of positive reinforcement, results in side effects that actually undermine safety in the long run. Documented side effects include lower morale, decreased teamwork, suppressed reporting of incidents and near misses, lower trust, and decreased engagement. These are exactly the kinds of things most organizations are working to increase! Returning to the scenario at the start of this chapter, Matt was on the safety committee (an example of discretionary behavior) but after his supervisor observed his work and gave him only negative feedback (despite the fact that he did several things correctly and he was new at the job), he resigned from the committee. When negative consequences are what employees experience most, resentment builds and discretionary effort is undermined.

A Better Way

By changing your focus to what people are doing well and purposely recognizing the safe behaviors you want more of, you will strengthen those safe behaviors, make them more consistent, and at the same time build relationships, trust, morale, and discretionary effort. But it isn't easy. It requires fighting the temptation to manage only exceptions. It requires being deliberate with your use of consequences rather than relying on the default approach of negative reinforcement. While it can be challenging, the payoff for your efforts will be enormous.

Myths & Misunderstandings About Positive Reinforcement

Before exploring *how* to use positive reinforcement most effectively, it's important to understand what positive reinforcement *is* and *is not*. There are many myths and misunderstandings about positive reinforcement. Most people have stereotypical ideas of what positive reinforcers are, often citing a pat on the back, praise, or money as prime examples. In fact, those things may be reinforcers or they may not be. It comes down to whether they work. A positive reinforcer is defined by its effect on behavior, so it can be *anything* that follows behavior that strengthens that behavior. Think of positive reinforcers as rebar in concrete

> Positive reinforcement is like rebar— it strengthens behavior.

structures. Rebar strengthens a structure. Reinforcement strengthens behavior. If your praise strengthens a behavior (makes it more likely to happen), then it is a positive reinforcer. If money doesn't have any impact on behavior, then it isn't a positive reinforcer. People may say they like it (who doesn't like money?) but that doesn't mean it influences the behavior you are interested in. Don't confuse what people like with what will strengthen their behavior.

Another misconception about positive reinforcement is that the bigger the reinforcer the more effective it will be. Some companies have tried using new cars in safety incentive programs believing that the large prize will motivate safe behavior. In fact, the size of the reinforcer is not the critical feature. A positive comment from someone you respect is often more powerful than the chance to win a large, tangible prize. Reinforcers can only strengthen behavior when they are closely linked to behavior. Safety incentives and prizes are often awarded to people for *not* having accidents rather than for specific, safe behaviors. Furthermore, the strength of reinforcers is based largely on immediacy and probability. An immediate consequence, one that happens while a person is engaging in a behavior or immediately afterward, is much more powerful than one that happens a few hours, days, or months later. This explains why people continue to eat potato chips when they know perfectly well that fat and sodium are unhealthy. The chips taste good *while we eat them;* our health is impacted at some later point in time. Add to that the element of probability—it is pretty certain that those chips are going to taste good, but not certain that our health will suffer for eating them. High-probability consequences are more powerful than low-probability consequences. This is why the threat of speeding tickets is so ineffective at getting most people to drive the speed limit. The probability of getting a speeding ticket is low. We "get away with it" most of the time. This is true of many at-risk behaviors at work. We get away with it—don't get hurt—most of the time.

If you take just a few ideas from this book, let this be one of them. When you understand the power of immediate and certain consequences, it reshapes your approach to managing behavior. You understand the power of daily safety interactions. The more you are out talking to your direct reports about what you have just observed them doing around safety, the more impact you will have. You don't need to give away cars, or create elaborate safety incentives, since those are future and uncertain consequences. Just go out, look for safe behaviors, and comment on them. Those more immediate, more certain consequences will have greater impact than any incentive at strengthening safe behavior. If you doubt the power of small but immediate and certain consequences, just think about some of the powerful reinforcers that unfortunately encourage at-risk behaviors. Many at-risk behaviors—failure to wear

> Daily safety interactions allow you to deliver immediate and certain consequences.

PPE, failure to tie off when working at height, lifting heavy objects alone rather than getting help, skipping steps in a procedure—are done because they are more comfortable, easier, and/or save time. These seemingly small reinforcers are extremely powerful because they are immediate and certain. Think of how many at-risk behaviors your crew engages in so they can save a few minutes.

Improving Your Reinforcement Skills

Using the science as a guide, here are some tips that will help you more effectively use positive reinforcement to strengthen critical safe behaviors.

- **Individualize it.** Reinforcement is not a one-size-fits-all proposition. What works for one person may not work for the next. If you follow the tips for building relationships with your crew, you will have a good idea of what might be reinforcing to each of your direct reports. For example, saying, "Your kids would be proud of you" would be reinforcing to someone you know who is trying to be a good role model for their children.

- **Be sincere.** Everyone can see through insincere attempts at reinforcement, so if you are going to say something positive, make sure you mean it. One way to ensure you come across as sincere is to be specific. For example, saying, "Thanks for helping out with safety today" may sound insincere but saying "I noticed you took extra time to point out the safe procedure to the new hire; I really appreciate that," sounds sincere.

- **Be specific.** Many supervisors think they do plenty of reinforcement because they say general, positive things like "Good job!" or "We had a safe day today." These statements don't tell individuals what they did well and therefore what they should continue to do. By pinpointing the specific behaviors you like and want more of, you increase effectiveness. For example you could say, "I noticed you rolled up the hoses and swept the floor before you left the work area. That is really going to help prevent tripping incidents in that area."

- **Deliver it immediately.** The more immediate reinforcement is, the more effective it is. A thumbs-up when you see someone tying off is more effective than talking to them at the end of the shift. Catch people in the act and reinforce.

- **Use it frequently.** It takes many reinforcers to make a habit. This is particularly true when someone is working to change an unsafe habit to a safe habit. The more frequently the behavior is reinforced, the faster it changes.

- **Use it to shape behavior.** Don't save reinforcement for above-and-beyond performance; use it to *build* above-and-beyond performance. By reinforcing progress in the right direction, you will help people build safer habits faster.

- **Avoid buts and sandwiches.** When possible, avoid mixing positive and constructive feedback. Pointing out what someone did well and then adding "but" often wipes out the reinforcing value of anything positive you said. Sandwiching negative feedback between positives is equally ineffective. Let your reinforcement stand alone.

- **Maintain at least a 4:1 ratio.** Good supervision involves both positive and negative consequences. It is the ratio that matters. Maintaining a 4:1 ratio of positives to negatives will help minimize the undesired side effects of the negatives and ensure you are using enough positives to strengthen critical behaviors. This is a general rule of thumb, not intended for each interaction. If you find yourself using more negatives with a direct report, look for what they are doing well or for improvements that you can positively reinforce. If you are using more positives with a direct report, don't actively look for something to criticize. A greater than 4:1 ratio is fine.

- **Ask more, tell less.** While telling a direct report what they have done well can be reinforcing, asking questions is another great way to strengthen behavior. Asking questions gives people a chance to tell you what they know (and you may be reinforced by what you learn when you listen).

- **Use tangibles sparingly.** While occasional tangibles (trinkets, ball caps, tickets to movies, lottery tickets, etc.) can add interest and enthusiasm, the bulk of your reinforcement should be social in nature. Verbal interactions that leave the employee feeling like what they are doing matters are the best reinforcers of all, and they are free.

START TODAY!

While it is tricky to do well, positive reinforcement is well worth working on. Not only will it strengthen safe behaviors (thus reducing injuries), it will also build engagement, build relationships, build trust, and improve morale. So where do you start? The biggest mistake most people make is not being specific enough. Start by pinpointing the behaviors you want.

CHAPTER 7

RESPOND CAREFULLY TO FAILURE

"An incident must not be seen as a failure or a crisis, either by management, or by colleagues. An incident is a free lesson, a great opportunity to focus attention and to learn collectively."—Sidney Dekker

Why This Matters

Your teenage daughter calls you from a party. She has been drinking. She knows you are going to be angry but she doesn't want to drive home or ride with any of her friends since they have been drinking too. How do you react? You're mad. You're disappointed. You can't believe she deceived you (she said she was going to the movies with girlfriends). Your knee-jerk reaction might be to yell and scream and tell her she is grounded until she is 25. What you *want* to say and what you *should* say are two very different things, but one thing is for certain: what you end up saying will influence your ability to help your daughter navigate future temptations of the teenage years.

She has engaged in some bad behavior (lying and drinking). But she has also done something good—she called you for a ride instead of driving intoxicated. The decision to lie and drink happened hours ago. The decision to call you happened minutes ago. The decision to call is the behavior you should choose to respond to. That is the behavior that is most likely to be strengthened or weakened by how you react. Remember, immediate consequences are the most powerful.

The corollary in safety is the moment your direct reports tell you about a minor safety incident or near miss. Like the moment your daughter calls from the party, what you do at that instant will determine whether or not you hear about future incidents and near misses. If you react to the incident instead of reacting to the *telling* about the incident, you are making a serious mistake.

While no one wants to hear about failure (failure in safety systems, failure in processes, failure in judgment), the silver lining in all forms of failure is that they are opportunities to learn. These undesirable safety events provide insight into how safety is really working, as opposed to how we think it is working. They uncover weaknesses in safety systems and processes that, in turn, enable changes to be made to prevent future incidents. Finding out your daughter is drinking is upsetting. But it is far better to know what she is really doing because that knowledge enables you to manage the behavior. It's upsetting to find out that your direct reports routinely ignore a critical safety procedure, but knowing the truth enables you to manage the behavior and build toward a safer future.

While these situations can be complicated, your reaction to the reporting of such events should be something like, "Thanks for telling me. Let's figure out how to prevent this from happening again." To be clear, I am not suggesting positive reinforcement for incidents, near misses, or unsafe actions; I am suggesting positive reinforcement for the honest reporting of those events.

> Positively reinforce honest reporting of bad news.

Reporting Near Misses

A great example of the importance of how management responds to undesired safety events is in near miss reporting. Most organizations understand the value of and work hard to create near miss reporting systems. Despite the time, energy, and resources put into them, near miss reporting systems often fail to live up to their potential. Once you understand behavior scientifically, you understand why. The desired behavior in near miss reporting is for employees to report any event that others might learn from, in order to prevent future incidents or injuries. Any safety event is an opportunity to learn, so any and all reports are encouraged.

Unfortunately, most organizations struggle to get

employees to report near misses. The ones that do get reported fall into one of three categories:

1. Minor near misses like paper cuts, bug bites, or a deer on the shoulder of the highway on the way to work
2. Very serious near misses that cannot be covered up or ignored
3. Near misses that had witnesses (thus failing to report is not an option)

Why is there such a gap between the intent of near miss reporting (report *any* event that others can learn from) and ultimate impact (a few minor incidents and a few major incidents with little in-between)? Unfortunately many near miss reporting systems end up discouraging the very behavior they require: reporting a situation where an injury or damage could have happened, but didn't. The systems—and those who implement the systems—unintentionally punish the reporting of significant near misses.

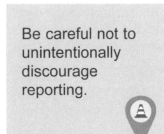

Be careful not to unintentionally discourage reporting.

Intentional and Unintentional Punishment

The science of behavior defines punishment as anything that follows behavior that decreases the frequency of the behavior. In everyday language, when bad things happen to people after they do something, they tend to stop doing it. When looking at what happens to most employees who report significant near misses it becomes clear that unintentional punishment is at work. Ask front-line employees and they will tell you that reporting a significant near miss leads to undesirable consequences for them. Rigorous investigations can feel like an inquisition to the person reporting. Phone calls from executives, while intended to show support and positive attention, can be very intimidating to the receiver. Publicized near miss bulletins can bring unwanted attention and embarrassment to the individual and/or team. In the worst case scenario, employees who report near misses are disciplined for their role in them. While management often denies that any negative consequences are associated with near miss reporting, the frequency of reporting—namely, the lack thereof—indicates otherwise.

Just Because It Isn't Punishing Doesn't Mean It Is Reinforcing

Even if there aren't punishing consequences associated with near miss reporting, that doesn't mean there are positive consequences. Near miss reporting is a voluntary activity. Management might say that it is a requirement; however, with so many employees working outside of close supervision, it is difficult to enforce. Voluntary activities require

Reporting your own mistakes is never positively reinforcing.

support by positive consequences. Unfortunately, reporting a near miss is not naturally positively reinforcing, therefore positive reinforcement must be built into near miss reporting processes. Without positive reinforcement, an employee faced with the decision between reporting and potentially being embarrassed, grilled, or even disciplined; or, saying nothing and avoiding all negative consequences, will opt for keeping quiet. Many will conclude it is much better to continue with the task at hand even when there was a close call or a learning opportunity that others could benefit from knowing.

It might seem that there is a powerful positive consequence for reporting a near miss and that is, preventing an injury on the part of a peer. While that is a positive consequence for most employees, it is a future and uncertain consequence and therefore not as powerful as we might hope. Add in the fact that reporting might lead to the more immediate negative consequences and it is no surprise organizations struggle to get near miss reporting to occur.

Reporting Incidents

From a consequence perspective, reporting a near miss is one thing, but reporting an actual incident takes it up a notch. The negative consequences for actual incidents are not only more likely, they are often more serious. It should be no surprise then that many organizations experience underreporting. While senior managers don't want to believe it, the truth is that underreporting is a relatively common phenomenon. It is safety's dirty little secret.

Again, if you understand behavior scientifically you understand why this is.

Negative consequences discourage people from reporting incidents. Many of those consequences are the same as those associated with near misses (blame, unpleasant investigations, embarrassment, discipline), but punishment is not the only culprit here. Another consequence undermines reporting and it masquerades as positive reinforcement—safety incentives.

Safety incentives are very popular and many people believe they are helpful. The truth is most safety incentives are not only *not* helpful, they are harmful. The typical safety incentive awards a prize or money for going a period of time without an injury. Some examples are crews get leather jackets if they go six months without a recordable injury, individuals who haven't had an incident in a month get their name entered in a drawing for a smart phone, year-end bonuses are based on reduction in incident rate.

These may seem like reasonable programs. After all, the goal is to eliminate incidents. The problem with incentives based on not having incidents is that employees can get the incentive in three possible ways:

1. Employees work safely and thus earn the reward through desired safe behavior. In this case the incentives are working the way we hope and intend; they are motivating safe behavior and that safe behavior is preventing incidents.

2. Employees engage in some or many at-risk behaviors but are lucky in that none of the at-risk behaviors result in an incident. In this

case the incentives are rewarding luck and possibly teaching employees that at-risk behaviors are okay—"It won't happen to me!"

3. Employees engage in at-risk behaviors and some of those at-risk behaviors result in incidents, but the incidents are not reported in order to avoid losing the incentive. In this case, incentives are motivating non-reporting of incidents.

In every one of my clients that has such incentives, frontline employees admit to me that they do not report all incidents because they don't want to lose the incentive. Importantly, they often emphasize that they don't want to ruin it for their peers. As one frontline employee put it, "How would you like to be the one who caused all your peers to lose five-hundred dollars?" If reporting a minor injury led to getting grilled (and possibly disciplined) by management and losing incentive money for yourself and all of your peers, would you report?

Learning from Behavior

As a frontline supervisor you probably can't change the incentive systems in your organization. You also most likely don't have a say in the near miss reporting systems and the consequences associated with those. So what can you do? You can try to shield your direct reports from some of the punishing consequences associated with those systems (e.g., public posting of near misses, being grilled about an incident over and over again). You can certainly try to offset some of the negative organizational consequences through your use of positive reinforcement. Remember, you have the advantage of being able to be more immediate and certain with your consequences. You can also try to educate managers and executives about the impact of unintended negative consequences for reporting near misses and incidents. But as a frontline supervisor your biggest opportunity to *learn from failure* happens even before the near miss or incident occurs. Your learning opportunity lies in daily behavior.

Rather than wait until something happens (a near miss or an incident), the ideal is for employees to report *precursor* events. Precursor events include hazardous conditions, faulty organizational systems, and gaps in safety practices. As discussed in Chapter 4, organizations usually have systems in place for reporting hazards. Opportunities to discuss faulty organizational systems must be created. Supervisors should ask questions to uncover system problems such as inadequate safety training, unclear procedures, or management strategies that encourage safety shortcuts. Gaps in safety practices are most often identified through observation. As a supervisor you see them, but those in the best position to see them are the frontline employees. Ideally, your team would be willing to talk about their own at-risk behavior. They would be willing to discuss times when they are tempted to take shortcuts, occasions when they forget to wear safety gear, situations where they don't report hazards, and reasons they don't

> Precursor events provide the best opportunities to learn and prevent incidents.

speak up when they see a peer do something unsafe. This would be the ultimate way to learn and improve because such behaviors are precursors to incidents and near misses. Getting such information requires a culture of trust. It also requires a *want to* environment rather than a *have to* environment around safety reporting and self-improvement. Given the negative consequences that dominate most safety systems, safety is clearly in the *have to* camp in most organizations. But it need not be this way.

Think about people who are passionate about sports. My mentor, Aubrey Daniels, is passionate about golf. He loves to golf and is always striving to get better. He reads about golf. He watches videos about golf. He hires golf pros for coaching. When he misses a shot he asks his golf partners what he did wrong. He pays close attention to his own behavior (grip, stance, swing) and constantly strives to improve. While it seems unlikely that we could get frontline employees to show that level of passion and commitment to improving safety and their own safe behaviors, we could certainly move in that direction. You might be thinking that it's impossible because safety isn't as fun as golf, but passion and enthusiasm are not a function of the activity. Think about playing slot machines. There is nothing inherently fun about sitting in front of a machine, pushing buttons and monitoring the display. In fact, on the surface it looks suspiciously like many jobs. But there are plenty of people who are passionate and enthusiastic about doing it—in fact they pay to do it! Passion and enthusiasm are a function of positive consequences. If we want more passion, commitment, reporting, self-analysis, peer coaching, and engagement in safety, then we need to make safety more positively reinforcing.

The bottom line message here is that there are safety-related behaviors that your direct reports do (or fail to do) every day that provide valuable learning, just as near misses and incidents do. In order to learn those lessons, your direct reports need to tell you about those safety-related behaviors. That requires creating a culture of trust and reinforcement within your work team. It requires creating an environment where your direct reports view you as their safety coach (like a golf pro) and therefore seek you out to help them improve (rather than hide from you to avoid trouble). Imagine a workplace where employees say, "Hey boss, come observe me and tell me if I am doing everything safely." It is possible.

Strategies to Encourage Reporting

Below are tips for increasing employees' willingness to report incidents, near misses, and precursor events, to improve organizational learning.

Analyze the current consequences. Look at what currently encourages or discourages reporting so you know what needs to change. (The next chapter will introduce the PIC/NIC Analysis® which is a great tool to do just that.)

Minimize the work. When reporting safety events is cumbersome or time-consuming, people are less likely to report. Make reporting as quick and easy as possible. Obviously, learning from events requires sufficient details, so some information gathering is inevitable. Just make it as quick and painless as possible.

Eliminate embarrassment. No one likes to admit that they messed up. Having the whole organization know about it makes it so much worse. Try to get the learning without identifying and/or embarrassing the person who experienced it firsthand. Protect anonymity when possible.

Make immediate consequences positive. The immediate consequence for reporting/discussing any undesired safety event should make the employee glad they reported. An angry outburst or look of disappointment from you will discourage reporting. Check your emotions and remember that your first priority is to reinforce the behavior of reporting.

Let people know it mattered. The best reinforcer for reporting a near miss, incident, or discussing a precursor event, is knowing it helped others avoid getting hurt, or improved safety in some way. The worst case scenario is reports that appear to go into the organizational black hole, never to be seen or heard about again. Publicizing improvements (without embarrassing anyone) helps cultivate a learning environment.

Admit your mistakes. You make mistakes too. A common mistake supervisors make involves inadvertently focusing on production, which contributes to employees rushing and taking shortcuts. For example, you may rush through a safety briefing because of production demands, unintentionally sending a message that production is more important. Your team will appreciate you acknowledging your missteps and how you learned from them, and will be more likely to do the same.

Ask questions to uncover learning. Sometimes people need prompting to discuss what has gone wrong. Here are some conversation starters that will help uncover learning opportunities.

- It must be hard to do ___ safely. How do you do it?
- When I did this job I was tempted to take ___ shortcut. How about you?
- How well did the training prepare you to do ___ safely?
- What happens when the job doesn't go as planned?
- Do you find that the procedure has enough detail to help you do ___ safely?

START TODAY!

Acknowledging that failure is inevitable but being relentless about learning from it is the hallmark of an exemplary safety culture. Regardless of where your organization is on this journey, you can create a culture of learning within your team. Two good places to start are analyzing existing consequences for reporting and admitting when you make mistakes. It will take time to make it okay for others to admit their mistakes so be patient and keep reinforcing.

 START >

CHAPTER 8

ELIMINATE BLAME

"Abolish all financial and professional penalties in the wake of an occurrence. Suspending practitioners after an incident should be avoided at all cost. These measures serve absolutely no purpose other than making incidents into something shameful, something to be kept hidden. If your organization has these kinds of rules in place, you can count on losing out on a lot of valuable safety information."—Sidney Dekker

Why This Matters

Blame is the enemy of safety improvement. All the strategies discussed in this book are undermined by blame. Blame damages relationships, destroys engagement, dampens openness, and dilutes learning.

Unfortunately, there is a legacy of blame in safety. When something bad happens there is usually a call to find out who is responsible. This is based partly on the belief that if you find the person responsible you can fix that person and therefore fix the problem. Rarely is it that simple. Most safety incidents are the coming together of a number of factors (conditions, behaviors, systemic weaknesses). To pin the blame on one person or one act is almost always overly simplistic. Even in cases where an employee clearly did something that contributed to the incident, blame (and the negative consequences that usually follow) rarely solves the problem. When "human error" is determined to be the cause or a contributing cause of an incident, it is important that we take the time to understand why the person did what they did. To say that an operator "failed to follow procedure" and assume that (1) explains what happened and (2) prevents it from happening again, is naïve.

In order to understand the human behavior element of any safety event and importantly, to learn how to prevent it from happening again, we need to do a better job of analyzing at-risk behavior. The PIC/NIC Analysis is a tool

Blame gets in the way of productive problem solving.

based on the science of behavior, that does just that. It helps us see the multiple causes of at-risk behavior, which then allows more productive problem solving.

How Do We Stop the Blame Game?

Eliminating blame requires adopting the belief that most people try to do a good job most of the time. People don't intentionally make mistakes. People don't want to get hurt. In my experience, employees involved in safety incidents were just trying to do a good job. They were just trying to get the product produced, meet the schedule, and/or keep the customer happy. After an incident it is easy to play armchair quarterback and point to what seems like obvious things they should have done. However, if you were in their shoes, doing what they were doing, knowing what they know, dealing with the distractions and pressures they were dealing with, you may well have done the same thing.

The PIC/NIC Analysis helps you put yourself in the performers' shoes so that you can understand the choices they make. It is a way to apply what we know about what makes consequences most powerful and to use that to analyze why behaviors occur or don't occur. It takes into account that every behavior has multiple consequences (some positive and some negative) and it is the balance of consequences that determines what people end up doing. Once you can accurately analyze consequences, you can begin to predict and change behavior.

We've discussed the fact that immediate and certain consequences are most powerful, but to more thoroughly and systematically analyze behavior, it is helpful to use the following model to categorize every consequence for a particular behavior.[1]

[1]Portions of this chapter are reprinted from *Safe by Accident* by Judy Agnew and Aubrey Daniels, with permission from Performance Management Publications (Atlanta).

> **Type of Consequence:**
>
> **P**ositive to the performer
>
> **N**egative to the performer
>
> **When the consequence follows the behavior:**
>
> **I**mmediately: while the behavior is happening or immediately after
>
> **F**uture: a few minutes, hours, days, or longer
>
> **Probability of the consequence occurring:**
>
> **C**ertain: the consequence will happen close to or at 100 percent
>
> **U**ncertain: the consequence only happens some of the time

POSITIVE VERSUS NEGATIVE A positive consequence is one that encourages more of the same behavior and a negative consequence (not to be confused with a negative reinforcer) is one that discourages more of the same behavior.

Whether a consequence is positive or negative varies from one individual to the next. We are all different in terms of whether particular consequences will have a positive or negative impact on us. For example, some people love public praise and will work to get more of it. Other people are embarrassed by it and will work hard to avoid any recognition in front of others.

IMMEDIATE VERSUS FUTURE Consequences that are immediate are much more powerful than those that are future. The farther away in time a consequence occurs following a behavior, the weaker is its influence on behavior. This is one of the reasons that the threatened consequence of chronic back pain is not very effective at persuading young, strong employees to bend and lift properly or to ask for help when lifting. Young people are relatively certain they will not hurt their backs the next time they lift something. Back injuries are often cumulative, so they may develop back problems after years of improper lifting, if they develop problems at all.

On the other hand, the immediate consequences for improper lifting (from the employee's point of view) include such immediate payoffs as saving time and effort, comfort, and looking strong and independent (if the alternative is asking for help).

CERTAIN VERSUS UNCERTAIN Consequences that are certain are much more powerful than those that are uncertain. A good example of a certain consequence is burning your hand if you touch a hot stove. This will happen every time you touch a hot stove. Anyone with children knows it usually takes only one experience for a child to learn not to touch the stove again. In this case a painful injury proves to be a powerful consequence because it is certain and immediate.

A good example of an uncertain consequence is suffering a head injury from not wearing a helmet when cycling. You could ride your bike without a helmet day after day for years and not get a head injury. Getting knocked off your bike and hitting your head is uncertain. Anyone who has tried to convince teenagers to wear a

> Immediate and certain consequences are the most powerful.

helmet (and actually buckle it up) understands this issue well. To defend their position, teenagers say, "I ride without a helmet all the time and nothing bad has happened." The uncertain nature of most injuries leads to the development of many unsafe habits.

PICS AND NICS Putting all the pieces together, we can analyze the power or strength of any consequence by determining whether it is positive or negative, immediate or future, certain or uncertain. As the diagram below shows, consequences that are both immediate and certain (regardless of whether they are positive or negative) are the most powerful.

Consequences that are positive, immediate, but uncertain, are the next most powerful. (Think of winning at a slot machine or catching a fish. Both of those are P,

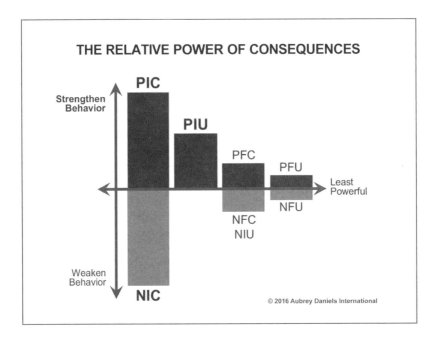

THE RELATIVE POWER OF CONSEQUENCES

© 2016 Aubrey Daniels International

I, but U and yet they are very powerful consequences.) Consequences that are negative, immediate, but uncertain are less powerful. Think of using intermittent punishment with your kids. It's less effective, right? Those consequences that are certain but future (whether positive or negative) are also less powerful. Finally, consequences that are both future and uncertain are the weakest of all.

PIC/NIC Analysis®

Aubrey Daniels International (ADI) created the PIC/NIC Analysis as a simple way to analyze any behavior. In safety, it usually shows how at-risk behavior is being encouraged by unplanned reinforcers and how safe behavior is usually being unintentionally discouraged. The PIC/NIC Analysis is very helpful in showing us all the various sources of consequences and how much impact they each have. It also helps us see how to arrange consequences in order to encourage safe over at-risk behavior.

In my experience, many PIC/NIC Analyses show that at-risk behaviors are unintentionally reinforced by management and peers who have a history of reinforcing working quickly without enough attention paid to safety. It also frequently highlights many barriers to safe behavior that make it difficult or impossible for employees to do the right thing. Finally, these analyses can show how antecedents can be better used to prompt safe behavior. It can be helpful to do a series of PIC/NIC Analyses to show the interconnectedness of antecedents and consequences in an organization.

Here is a common example. Frontline employees some-times speed while operating equipment.

PIC/NIC ANALYSIS®

Operator At-Risk Behavior:
Speeding while operating equipment

Antecedents	Consequences	P/N	I/F	C/U
Schedule demands	Get work done faster	P	I	C
Someone waiting for equipment	Going fast (more fun)	P	I	C
Boss talked about high volume of work to be completed today	Avoid being teased by peers for being too slow	P	I	C
	Stay on schedule	P	I	C
	Praise from boss for productivity	P	F	C
	Get hurt	N	I	U

As you can see by this analysis, there are four PICs and one PFC for speeding. There is only one negative and it is uncertain, therefore weaker. Closer inspection shows that three of the positive consequences for at-risk behavior are related to better productivity. The antecedents also show a pattern of focus on production. This tells us that there are probably many intentional and unintentional ways that working quickly (and therefore getting more work done—or perceiving that you are) is reinforced in this workplace.

Does that mean the supervisor is to blame? No. Below is a PIC/NIC Analysis on the supervisor's behavior. A common at-risk behavior that supervisors engage in is praising employees for high productivity (or meeting deadlines) without checking to make sure the work was done without taking safety shortcuts. Why would a supervisor who cares about safety do this?

PIC/NIC ANALYSIS®

Supervisor At-Risk Behavior:
Praising operators for productivity without attending to safety

Antecedents	Consequences	P/N	I/F	C/U
Schedule demands	Feel like I am managing productivity	P	I	C
High volume of work today	Getting product out	P	I	C
Boss asking about whether the work is getting done	Easier to manage by results	P	I	C
Haven't had an incident for months	Stay on schedule	P	F	C
Too busy with paperwork to do safety observations	Job done and no one was hurt	P	I	C
	Increased incentive money	P	F	U
	Praise from my boss	P	F	C
	Avoid conflict about safety issues	P	I	U
	Operator gets hurt	N	F	U

In this analysis, like the operator analysis, there are more positive consequences than negative for making safety communications secondary and the positives are more powerful than the one negative. There are also antecedents focused on productivity. The supervisor (like the operator) is choosing the at-risk behavior because the antecedents and consequences support doing so.

This analysis can be done at all levels of the organization. Let's look at what might be going on at the higher levels where decisions are being made about organizational systems such as incentive systems, which are implicated in the supervisor analysis.

PIC/NIC ANALYSIS®

Executive At-Risk Behavior:
Weighing productivity much higher than safety in an incentive system

Antecedents	Consequences	P/N	I/F	C/U
Pressure from Board of Directors to improve productivity	Seeing good production report	P	I	C
Pressure from shareholders to be more efficient	Better long-term productivity	P	F	C
Market pressures to be more competitive	Increase profits	P	F	C
Incident rate is better than it has been in the past	Company stays competitive	P	F	C
	Shareholders are happy	P	F	C
	Increase accidents	N	F	U

In each case, the performer (operator, supervisor, executive) is doing what makes sense given the antecedents and consequences operating on their behavior. They are doing what appears to be the best for the company; after all, companies must produce to stay in business. As you can see, it is all too easy for leaders to have good intentions regarding safety, but to unintentionally have a negative impact.

Eliminating Blame Is a PICNIC

The PIC/NIC Analysis takes the blame out of safety by uncovering the real causes of behavior. The analysis helps us see that it does no good to simply blame the frontline employee (or the frontline supervisor) for at-risk behavior. To discipline the operator for speeding or the supervisor for failing to manage the speeding isn't getting at the heart of the issue—that the organization pushes productivity over safety. Blaming those at the front line is not only unproductive, it is unjust.

A more productive and just approach is to understand, through the PIC/NIC Analysis, what antecedents and consequences are contributing to the problem and making changes to those. Sometimes the antecedents and consequences are embedded in a system and sometimes they are directly issued by management, but either way, the analysis enables them to be

> Blame antecedents and consequences, not people.

examined and changed to positively alter behavior. Rather than blame the people, the PIC/NIC Analysis redirects the blame to the antecedents and consequences and helps us make changes to improve.

START TODAY!

Take one of the critical behaviors you identified in Chapter 5 and try doing a PIC/NIC Analysis® on the at-risk behavior that is happening instead. Once you understand why people do the at-risk behavior, you will be better positioned to help them improve. Be sure to look at the behaviors from the performer's perspective, and include the performer if you can.

CHAPTER 9

CONSIDER SAFETY IN EVERY DECISION

Everything you do as a leader could have implications for safety.

Why This Matters

So far we have covered some concrete steps you can take to improve your safety leadership. Considering safety in every decision is a little harder to get your hands around. Let's start with some examples of what happens when safety isn't considered in organizational decisions.

Operators in a manufacturing facility had been responsible for a block of machines, both operating the machines and doing minor maintenance. They had a sense of ownership over their work area. In order to shorten new hire training time, management decided to simplify the role of machine operators. Operators worked together running all machines or doing minor maintenance, not both. The decision resulted in an increase in slip/trip hazards as a result of housekeeping violations. Management was frustrated that operators "didn't seem to care about safety anymore."

To meet year-end budget numbers, a transportation company limited inventory in the maintenance shop. Without access to the necessary parts, mechanics couldn't do some important repairs, such as change out worn tires.

A company instituted staggered start times to better meet demand and adapt to differing production schedules. Pre-shift safety meetings became difficult to schedule and ended up being poorly attended and often skipped altogether.

In order to provide more predictable schedules for supervisors, a food manufacturer chose to have set schedules for supervisors rather than have them rotate days and nights with the crews. This resulted in supervisors not being able to develop relationships with their crews; in some cases they didn't even know their names. Most of the supervisors reverted to negative reinforcement ("do it, or else") for managing safety.

Quality problems resulted in an organization losing market share. In response, a new quality program was introduced that included a management scorecard heavily weighted on quality (including both leading and lagging quality metrics) and linked to a bonus. While safety was included, the metric was incident rate. Leaders started spending considerably more time on quality.

The Ripple Effect

Organizations are interconnected systems. A change in one area inevitably has impact in other areas, often unanticipated. While it is impossible to anticipate all the ways a decision will influence safety, it is important to try.

To survive, organizations must constantly improve and that means constant change. As competition gets tougher, products and services need to be delivered faster, cheaper, and with better quality. While senior leaders are always concerned about safety, their job is to keep the company profitable—to make money. It is easy to see how well-intended leaders make decisions that are good for the business but end up having negative implications for safety. Some examples include decisions that alter the following: production levels, quality requirements, procurement processes, preventative maintenance systems, management scorecards, incentive systems, staffing levels, and supervisory spans of control. Changes to any of these can unintentionally increase hazardous conditions, disrupt process safety, alter safety leadership practices, or foster at-risk behavior at the front line. The impact is not always direct. For example, a change in the preventative maintenance system that is intended to improve efficiency may reduce thoroughness and lead to increased hazards. A change in a management scorecard can tip the balance toward leaders spending more time on quality and by default, less on safety.

Smaller Ripples

As a frontline supervisor your decisions likely have smaller ripple effects than those of senior leaders whose decisions impact large parts of the organization, but there is a ripple nonetheless. Rather than influencing safety through organizational systems, your decisions are likely to have a more direct impact on conditions and on the day-to-day antecedents and consequences for behavior. Examples of such decisions include which employees to pair up for a job, when to order replacement parts, whether to work your crew overtime, how many people to assign to a job, how often you will check in during a task, and time estimates given to management regarding completion of work. The good news is that you have an advantage over senior leaders when it comes to anticipating the ripple effect. Senior leaders don't spend a lot of time observing the work being done at the front line. You do. You see firsthand the hazardous conditions and the safe and at-risk behavior and that puts you in a better position to anticipate what the ripples might be, and make adjustments.

The Crystal Ball

The closest thing there is to a crystal ball that enables anticipation of all the ways a decision will impact safety-related behaviors is knowledge of the impact of antecedents and consequences, especially PICs and NICs. Being able to analyze what antecedents and consequences are currently supporting safety behavior allows you to better analyze what will happen to those antecedents and consequences once a new decision is implemented, thereby allowing you to analyze what is likely to happen to the safe behaviors. In the first example at the start of this chapter, operators took pride in keeping their work areas clean and running well. Once there were multiple people working the same area, cleaning up became less reinforcing because too often someone else came along and messed it up again. In the example of the management scorecard heavily weighted on quality, leaders focused more on quality and as long as they weren't having accidents they didn't do much with safety. Furthermore, with management's heavy focus on quality, frontline employees focused more on quality behaviors and less on safety.

It is important to remember that accurate predictions are based not on the intended impact of the management decision, but on the change in day-to-day antecedents and consequences and thus, safety behaviors of leaders and frontline employees. The PIC/NIC Analysis is a great tool to help make these predictions. An additional way to help you predict is to ask the people who are affected by the decision.

> When you understand PICs and NICs you can better predict behavior.

Ask the People Who Do the Work

This may sound obvious but it is remarkable how infrequently it is done. Talking to your direct reports and asking what the impact of a decision will be can provide insights you might never think of on your own. You can also include them in a PIC/NIC Analysis to more accurately anticipate how the changes will impact safety.

Clearly it isn't always possible to include frontline employees for two reasons. First, you can't always share decisions prior to making them. Second, people can't always anticipate how something will change their behavior until they experience it. While it won't always help, there may be times when getting input from your direct reports can help avoid safety problems.

Be Flexible

Despite your best efforts you will still make decisions that have unanticipated negative effects on safety. If possible, be prepared to pull back and make changes once the impact is observed. This is an opportunity to admit your mistakes, and show how you learn from them, and put safety above all else.

It is important to note that assessing the impact of a decision requires observing the impact on incident precursors such as hazardous conditions and safe and at-risk behavior. Avoid the mistake of assuming that a lack of incidents and/or near misses is sufficient evidence that a decision is not adversely impacting safety. Remember, groups can go long periods of time without incidents despite the presence of hazardous conditions and/or at-risk behavior.

Questions to Help You Consider Safety in Every Decision

One of the best ways to consider safety in decisions is to ask yourself a series of questions that help you think through all of the implications. The most obvious question is, "Will this decision impact safety, and how?" But the answer can be elusive. Here are some questions to help get at the answer when it isn't so obvious. The questions are organized around some common, general contributors to safety incidents.

Preparation
- Does the decision negatively impact training?
- Will it lead to new employees being put on the job too soon?
- Will it prevent or discourage pre-job planning or hazard assessment?

Rushing
- Does the decision encourage working faster?
- Does it impose tighter deadlines?
- Does it add steps or add work, without more time to complete the work?

Resources
- Does the decision reduce manpower and, if so, what implications will that have for safety?
- Does it add or remove tools, PPE, or machinery that may impact safety?
- Does it reduce supervision and thus opportunities for safety interactions and feedback?

- Does it negatively impact preventative maintenance or housekeeping?
- Does it impact safety resources like PPE, training,
or safety personnel?
- Will there be less experienced employees in jobs
without mentors or close supervision?

Distraction

- Will the decision add complexity to the tasks that
will distract employees from safety?
- Will it result in additional work, processes, or
procedures that will distract?
- Will it require multitasking that will be a distraction?

Fatigue

- Will the decision increase fatigue?
- Will it negatively impact break schedules?

Complacency

- Will the decision reduce stimulation and lead to
people not attending to what they are doing?
- Will it increase the temptation to look at cell
phones or other distractions?

START TODAY!

You can start improving your safety leadership with this simple step—ask the fundamental question every time you make a decision, "Will this decision impact safety, and how?"

START >

Questions to Help Consider Safety in Every Decision
* Will this decision impact safety, and how?

Preparation
- Does the decision negatively impact training?
- Will it lead to new employees being put on the job to soon?
- Will it prevent or discourage pre-job planning or hazard assessment?

Rushing
- Does the decision encourage working faster?
- Does it impose tighter deadlines?
- Does it add steps or add work, without more time to complete the work?

Resources
- Does the decision reduce manpower and, if so, what implications will that have for safety?
- Does it add or remove tools, PPE, or machinery that may impact safety?
- Does it reduce leadership and thus opportunities for safety interactions and feedback?
- Does it negatively impact preventative maintenance or housekeeping?
- Does it impact safety resources like PPE, training, or safety personnel?
- Will there be less experienced employees in jobs without mentors or close supervison?

Distraction
- Will the decision add complexity to the tasks that will distract employees from safety?
- Will it result in more work, processes, or procedures that will distract?
- Will it require multitasking that will be a distraction?

Fatigue
- Will the decision increase fatigue?
- Will it negatively impact break schedules?

Complacency
- Will the decision reduce stimulation and lead to people not attending to what they are doing?
- Will the temptation to look at cell phones or other distractions increase?

CHAPTER 10

SET YOURSELF UP FOR SUCCESS

"The secret of getting ahead is getting started."
—Mark Twain

Why This Matters

Hopefully you have read some things in this book that you want to do differently to improve your safety leadership. Like any behavior-change effort (increasing exercise, healthy eating, being more organized), getting started is the easy part; keeping it going is the hard part. As noted in the first chapter, just reading this book won't guarantee change. To turn the tips in this book into habits, you need to work on them over time. To ensure you keep working on them over time, you need a plan. If your company is working with ADI, we will help you with a positive accountability process. If not, this chapter will provide some ideas for building a plan to help you succeed.

Obstacles to Success

Many things get in the way of improvement efforts but here are the big three.

Time—The one thing no supervisor has enough of, is time. The front line is where it all comes together; where organizational plans get executed and the products and services come to life. Frontline supervisors are the linchpins who coordinate it all. All of those responsibilities mean you are busy—way too busy. It is hard enough dealing with the daily demands of just getting the work done, let alone working on relationships, ensuring hazards get fixed, identifying critical safe behaviors, providing timely and helpful feedback, finding effective ways to reinforce safe behaviors, and considering safety in every decision. Even when you are motivated to improve, it's hard.

Traditional Accountability—Given there isn't enough time to do everything you need or want to do each day, you have to prioritize. You likely make choices about how to spend your time based on what you are held accountable for. The problem is that what most managers hold supervisors accountable for around safety isn't compatible with the kind of leadership behaviors outlined in this book. Rather, supervisors are usually held accountable for some version of incident rate (e.g., TRIR, or LTI). Basically, most supervisors are held accountable for *not having accidents* in their work areas. On the surface this makes sense. After all, that is the goal—preventing injury in the workplace. While it is the ultimate goal, it doesn't make a good accountability goal. Why? For the same reasons it isn't good to celebrate number of days without a lost time injury…because there is more than one way to achieve the goal. A supervisor could do very little around safety and go for months, even years without his/her crew having an incident. They could be safe through luck, they could be safe in spite of the supervisor, or they could simply not report incidents. The bottom line is that traditional safety accountability doesn't set you up to work on the proactive safety leadership behaviors in this book.

> Lagging metrics encourage reactive safety leadership.

Lack of Reinforcement—We all do what we get reinforced for doing. If you get most of your reinforcement for focusing on productivity and not safety, then you will focus more on productivity. Just as positive reinforcement is critical for strengthening frontline safe behaviors, it is also critical for strengthening your safety leadership behaviors. Without reinforcement for the behaviors you learned in this book, you won't persist, even if you truly believe it is the right thing to do. Most of us think eating healthy food and exercising regularly is the right thing to do but few of us do it consistently. It comes down to what we get reinforced for.

Overcoming the Obstacles

Here are some tips for overcoming the big three obstacles.

Carve out Time. At the risk of sounding overly simplistic, the way to find time to improve your safety leadership is to carve out dedicated time in your schedule every day. Anyone who exercises regularly will tell you that the key to success is to have time blocked out in your daily schedule *in advance* and don't let anything interfere. Block out time each and every day to go out and interact with your direct reports and a few minutes afterward to follow up on anything that comes from those interactions. If your direct reports work elsewhere, then carve out time for phone calls at least a few times a week. Make sure these calls or face-to-face interactions are about safety. Have specific things you are going to observe for, ask about, and talk about around safety. They don't have to be long conversations; they might just be a few minutes. Just make sure to do it. Observing and coaching direct reports is the essence of good supervision. These activities are not "extra" work to be relegated to the, "I'll do it if I have time" category. In the big picture, regular safety interactions with your direct reports are more important than much of the email, paperwork, and meetings that consume too much supervisory time. And your boss is likely to agree.

Practice Proactive Accountability. To truly impact safety, leaders at all levels should be held accountable for what they are doing to prevent accidents—for their safety leadership behaviors—rather than just for a lack of incidents. If your organization has such an accountability system, then you are set. If instead, your organization holds leaders accountable for not having incidents (lagging metrics like incident rate), then you will have to create your own accountability system. Ideally, your boss will work with you to develop positive accountability for safety leadership behaviors you both agree are important. This can and should be part of your ongoing development. After all, safety leadership behaviors are just good leadership behaviors. If you are not in a situation where you can work with your boss, you can set up peer accountability with another supervisor. Some tips for doing so are below. The bottom line is that you need regular check-ins with another person who will hold you accountable for doing these important behaviors.

Build in Reinforcement Opportunities. Positive reinforcement doesn't have to come from your boss. It can come from peers and direct reports, so try to tap into those reinforcement sources by sharing what you are doing and soliciting feedback. Tell your crew about some of the things you have been trying to do to make safety easier for them and ask if it has made a difference. Share some of the changes you have made with a peer and ask what they think about them. You are likely to get some helpful feedback and enough reinforcement to keep you going. Another source of reinforcement is the natural reinforcement of seeing improvements as a result of your efforts. Some signs that what you are doing is working are the signs of frontline engagement outlined in Chapter 2:

- Increased participation in safety discussions
- Better planning for and anticipating hazards
- Actively working to keep peers safe
- Increased reporting of hazards and other safety issues
- Increased near miss reporting
- Challenging decisions that negatively impact safety

Consider improvement in any of these areas (no matter how small) as a sign that what you are doing is working, and let that encourage you to do more. Sometimes the business of daily life distracts us from seeing progress. Be sure to look for it because it will fuel further progress.

Systematic Safety Leadership Accountability

The science of behavior and our collective years of experience at ADI has taught us the importance of helping our clients build positive accountability systems to ensure continuous improvement. We normally work with natural work teams of managers and direct reports (e.g., a manager and a team of supervisors) to establish regular, structured meetings in which everyone shares examples of their safety leadership efforts, and the impact they are having. These brief meetings allow all supervisors and managers to get feedback, reinforcement, and suggestions for improvement from others who are also working on improving their safety leadership skills. These meetings (we call them *Debriefs*), serve to hold leaders accountable for doing the coaching they know they need to do, provide reinforcement for doing so, and enable the all-important refinement of leadership skills.

If you are reading this book because your organization is embarking on a safety leadership initiative with ADI, then you will be participating in a positive accountability process as described above. If you are reading this book on your own, or without ADI consulting support, then you can build your own positive accountability process. As noted above, ideally you can work with at least one other person such as your boss or a peer. Encourage a colleague to read this book and then plan some regular opportunities to hold each other accountable, reinforce each other's behaviors, and improve together.

Here are some tips for building positive accountability with others:

- **Plan frequent contact.** Weekly is ideal. Less frequent contact allows too much room for procrastination and drift.

- **Be consistent.** Meet the same day and the same time if possible and don't let anything short of a full-on emergency interfere.

- **Keep the meetings short and laser-focused on safety leadership skills.** Don't allow other issues to bleed into the discussion.

- **Build positive reinforcement into the process.** It is all too easy for such meetings to devolve into critiques. The goal is to reinforce and shape gradual improvement. There is no such thing as being perfect, and all efforts provide learning opportunities.

- **Plan your next steps.** After reviewing what you did, and how it worked to improve safety, plan what you will try during the upcoming week (or tomorrow, ideally).

Including other people in your change effort will make you (and them) more likely to succeed.

Deciding Where to Start

Every organization is at a different place in their safety journey, and each supervisor is as well. You need to assess where you are and what a good first step is, for you. Below are some client examples that outline where supervisors started and the reasons they started where they did.

Hazardous Workplace—This organization wanted to improve safe behaviors and engagement at the front line but had no formal hazard identification and remediation system. Frontline employees complained that the workplace was unsafe and weren't willing to get more engaged until management took better care of hazards. They started by developing a strong hazard-remediation system, which built trust and led to a willingness on the part of the front line to get more involved in safety.

Old School Safety—This organization had a very "old school" approach to safety leadership, including a heavy focus on using negative consequences around compliance with safety rules, and poor management-hourly employee relationships. They started with working on improving relationships by asking supervisors and managers to provide positive reinforcement when hourly employees complied with rules.

Wasting Reinforcement—This organization had good management-hourly relationships, and understood the importance of positive reinforcement, but supervisors reinforced easy-to-see behaviors which were already at habit (such as wearing hard hats) rather than behaviors that needed improvement. They started by pinpointing critical behaviors that would prevent the most frequent injuries. They then focused their reinforcement on those behaviors, tracking them over time so they could see improvement.

Poor Feedback and Reinforcement Skills—This organization encouraged all leaders to do behavioral observations daily but the quality of observations and feedback were poor. They started by working on improving the feedback and positive reinforcement skills of supervisors.

You might see yourself and/or your organization in some of these examples, or you might go back through the chapters of the book and look for your biggest improvement opportunities there.

START TODAY!

You can start improving your safety leadership by adopting any of the tips in this book. Start small because small victories will reinforce further effort. As stated in the introduction, if you make only one change, let it be this— increase your use of positive reinforcement. Consistent use of positive reinforcement for safety-related behaviors is the most powerful supervisory tool available. You will be amazed at the impact it will have on improving safety, building relationships, encouraging engagement, and making work more enjoyable.

Start today. **Start right now!**

ADDITIONAL RESOURCES

The easy part of this process is reading the material. The challenge is being diligent in using these tools and techniques. But in doing so, you will be surprised by how much more effective you become.

— J.W. (Jim) Latham III
Director of Positively CONSOL
CONSOL Energy

SAFETY ASSESSMENT SERVICES

ADI's Safety Assessment Services help organizations get an accurate picture of their safety leadership and safety culture. Assessment information is collected via surveys as well as on-site analysis conducted by ADI consultants. Our Safety Culture Survey assesses how the company as a whole manages and supports safety. Our Safety Leadership Survey provides feedback to each leader (supervisors and above) in the organization on how well they lead and manage safety. An on-site assessment by ADI consultants provides a more in-depth view of an organization's safety culture. Our clients use these assessments to establish a baseline for safety culture improvement, assess their readiness for BBS and/or Safety Leadership implementations, to review the effectiveness of existing BBS processes, and/or to gain a behavioral perspective on the effectiveness of their safety systems and processes (e.g., near miss reporting systems).

Whether you choose to use surveys, the on-site assessment or both, your organization will receive invaluable insight on organizational strengths and opportunities for improvement. ADI's surveys and assessments provide clients with an accurate picture of their safety culture as well as clear, actionable recommendations for improvement.

www.aubreydaniels.com/Safety-Surveys

SAFETY LEADERSHIP TRAINING AND COACHING

Effective leadership is key to safety improvement. From front-line supervisors to executives, Aubrey Daniels International (ADI) helps leaders maximize their impact through training and real-time coaching.

ADI works with leaders to:

- Manage safety with proactive, behavior-based metrics.
- Replace low-impact leader behaviors with high-impact activities.
- Use science to understand at-risk behavior and management's role in it.
- Engineer positive reinforcement into the workplace to increase safe behaviors at all levels.
- Analyze organizational systems and align them in support of safety.
- Ensure existing safety management programs effectively deliver desired outcomes.
- Develop coaching skills that build engagement and improve performance.

To become exemplary safety leaders who build high-performing safety cultures, leaders must engage in the right behaviors. Good intentions are not enough.

Could your organization benefit from improved safety leadership?

www.aubreydaniels.com/safety-leadership

info@aubreydaniels.com

SUGGESTED READING

BOOKS

Agnew, Judy and Snyder, Gail. *Removing Obstacles to Safety.* Atlanta: Performance Management Publications, 2008.

Agnew, Judy L. and Daniels, Aubrey C. *Safe By Accident? Take the Luck Out of Safety: Leadership Practices that Build a Sustainable Safety Culture.* Atlanta: Performance Management Publications, 2010.

Daniels, Aubrey C. *Bringing Out the Best in People.* New York: McGraw-Hill, 2016.

Daniels, Aubrey C., and Daniels, James E. *Measure of a Leader.* New York: McGraw-Hill, 2007.

Daniels, Aubrey C. *Other People's Habits: How to Use Positive Reinforcement To Bring Out The Best in People Around You.* Atlanta: Performance Management Publications, 2007.

Daniels, Aubrey C. and Bailey, Jon S. *Performance Management: Changing Behavior that Drives Organizational Effectiveness.* Atlanta, GA: Performance Management Publications, 2014.

Dekker, S. *Just Culture: Balancing Safety and Accountability.* Burlington, VT: Ashgate Publishing Company, 2007.

Latham, Glenn. *The Power of Positive Parenting.* UT: P&T Ink, 1990.

Lattal, Alice Darnell, and Clark, Ralph W. *A Good Day's Work.* NY: McGraw-Hill, 2006.

Maloney, Michael. *Teach Your Children Well.* MA: QLC Educational Services, Cambridge Center of Behavioral Studies,1998.

Marquet, L. David. *Turn the Ship Around! A True Story of Turning Followers into Leaders.* New York: Portfolio/ Penguin, 2012.

Reason, J.T. *Managing the Risks of Organizational Accidents.* Burlingon, VT: Ashgate Publishing Company, 1997.

ARTICLES

Agnew, Judy (2012). Effective Keys to Creating and Sustaining a Safety Culture. *PM eZine,* www.pmezine.com.

Agnew, Judy (2010). Employees Have Spoken . . . Fear and Failed Leadership Prove Disastrous in Safety. *Aubrey Daniels' Blog.*

Agnew, Judy (August, 2013). Relationships and Safety: What's the Link? *Facility Safety Management,* 22-23.

Daniels, Aubrey (2010). Relationships & Safety: Is There a Link? *Aubrey Daniels' Blog,* www.aubreydaniels-blog.com.

Martin & Black (September, 2015). Preventing Serious Injuries & Fatalities. *Professional Safety,* Volume 60, Issue 9.

Uhl, David (2012). Turn Up to Learn: Leadership in High-hazard Industries. *PM eZine,* www.pmezine.com.

PERFORMANCE MANAGEMENT PUBLICATIONS
ADDITIONAL TITLES

Safe By Accident?
Judy Agnew
Aubrey C. Daniels

Removing Obstacles to Safety
Judy Agnew
Gail Snyder

Bringing Out the Best in People
Aubrey C. Daniels

Measure of a Leader
Aubrey C. Daniels
James E. Daniels

Other People's Habits
Aubrey C. Daniels

Oops! 13 Management Practices that Waste Time and Money
Aubrey C. Daniels

Performance Management
(5th edition)
Aubrey C. Daniels
Jon S. Bailey

You Can't Apologize to a Dawg
Tucker Childers

Behaving Well
Edmund Fantino

Pay for Profit
William Abernathy

The Sin of Wages
William Abernathy

Human Performance Diagnostics
William Abernathy

For more titles and information call **1.800.223.6191**
or visit our website
www.PManagementPubs.com

ABOUT ADI

Founded in 1978, and headquartered in Atlanta, GA, Aubrey Daniels International (ADI) provides clients with the tools and methodologies to help move people toward positive, results-driven accomplishments and improve their business:

- **Assessments:** scientific analyses of the impact of systems, processes, structures, and practices, on performance
- **Safety Solutions:** surveys, assessments, behavior-based safety, safety culture and safety leadership training, and coaching
- **Executive Coaching**: helping executives apply a behavioral lens to improve their impact
- **Expert Consulting:** specialized, hands-on direction and support
- **Precision Leadership:** leadership training and coaching
- **Coaching for Rapid Change®**: a systematic process for focusing managers and leaders to shape positive performance
- **Surveys**: a complete suite of proprietary surveys
- **Certification:** ADI-endorsed mastery of client skills in our key products, processes, and/or technology
- **Seminars & Webinars:** a variety of engaging programs
- **Scorecards & Incentive Pay:** an alternative to traditional incentive-pay systems
- **Speakers:** accredited and celebrated thought leaders
- **Blitz Precision Learning®:** web-based application for developing, delivering, and administering training lessons

REGISTER YOUR BOOK

Register your copy of *A Supervisor's Guide to (Safety) Leadership* and receive exclusive reader benefits. Visit the website below and click on the **Register Your Book** link above the ADI storefront. Registration is free.

ABOUT THE AUTHOR

Judy Agnew is a recognized thought leader in the field of behavior-based safety, safety leadership, safety culture, and performance management. She is an expert consultant who works with clients to create behavioral interventions that ensure organizations are safe by design. As Senior Vice President of Safety Solutions at Aubrey Daniels International (ADI), Judy partners with clients to create behavior-based interventions that are grounded in the science of behavior and use positive, practical approaches that lead to long-term sustainability.

Judy has presented at major safety conferences, including the American Society of Safety Engineers, National Safety Council and Behavioral Safety Now, as well as other key corporate events. She is frequently interviewed for national and trade publications and has been featured in *Occupational Health and Safety* and *Industrial Hygiene News* to name a few. She is the author of two other highly regarded safety books, *Removing Obstacles to Safety* (with Gail Snyder) and *Safe by Accident? Take the Luck out of Safety: Leadership Practices that Build a Sustainable Safety Culture* (with Aubrey Daniels). Judy is also the recipient of 2011 Outstanding Contribution Award from the Organizational Behavior Management Network, which recognizes her significant contributions to the field of behavior analysis.